The Pond on My Windowsill

The Pond
on My Windowsill

by Christopher Reynolds
with drawings by the author

Forward and Appendix
by John C. Pallister, Ph.D.
American Museum of Natural History, New York City

Pantheon Books

Contents

Foreword

An aquarium of fish is always a delightful and pleasant amusement in any home. One may relax and watch the continual movement and the flashing colors of these active creatures. But an insect aquarium is a much more exciting and fascinating aquarium to have. And Christopher Reynolds, in his book, *The Pond on My Windowsill,* will tell you how he keeps an insect aquarium.

Most boys and girls will get a great deal of satisfaction from setting up an insect aquarium in their homes. Not only will they have the fun of going out to the ponds and streams in search of plants and little creatures to bring back, but there will also be the fun of the search itself, even though it will tax their skill to capture these little creatures. They will also get acquainted with them in the field, and will then become familiar with their daily lives, unfolding before their eyes. Not too much is known about the intimate life of many of the water insects, and it may happen that the budding scientists may even discover something that will contribute to our knowledge of the insects.

I can heartily recommend this book to young people and their parents as a clear and concise guide for setting up and stocking an insect aquarium.

Although this book is by an English writer, and is about the insect life in the ponds and streams of England, American boys and girls will find that the creatures mentioned, in most cases, will have very close relatives in the United States, as well as in other places around the world. This presents an interesting problem for the student. Although closely related, the American plants and insects may present somewhat different habits, because they have developed in a different environment. These habits should be more thoroughly studied and recorded. This is why I have provided an Appendix for this edition.

John C. Pallister, Ph.D., Research Associate
Department of Entomology
American Museum of Natural History
New York City

Introduction

The pond indoors on my windowsill contains a variety of small creatures. At any time of the year some of these are to be seen swimming among the stems and leaves of water plants, gliding over large stones which rise like miniature mountains, or crawling over the gravel bed of their watery world.

Occasionally I put into this pond a dead worm that I have picked from the wet pavement after rain. This provides food for many of the creatures. Small black flatworms emerge from under the stones and glide over the gravel toward it, waving their heads from side to side as they test the direction from which the scent of the worm is coming. Water beetles quickly discover the scent as it disperses through the water, and they swim in ever closer circles over the worm until they join the flatworms at the feast. Freshwater shrimps come sidling up, and leeches come looping over the gravel or swimming in graceful undulations to join the other creatures. Caddisfly larvae, jerking their cases of small sticks, leaves, little stones, or snail shells over the gravel, converge on the worm. Finally the water snails find their way, until the worm is completely covered with a mass of feeding creatures.

The next day a ghostly, translucent, bluish-white outer skin is all that is left of the dead worm.

Not all the creatures spend the whole of their lives in this pond. In spring and summer the young of dragonflies and damselflies, which have completed their growing stage in the form of what are called nymphs, climb up stems and come to rest several inches above the water. The fully grown nymphs of mayflies swim to the surface; and caddisfly pupae, which have bitten their way out from their sealed up cases after a resting period, row themselves up with a pair of oar-like legs and climb on to floating leaves. Then I can watch the wonderful transformation which these creatures undergo as they emerge from the husks of their underwater form. I can see them gradually expand their wings as fully developed insects.

This pond on my windowsill is, of course, an aquarium. I call it a pond because I have tried, as far as I can, to reproduce the natural conditions of a pond. There is no better way of studying living creatures than to make observations out of doors, watching them in their natural surroundings. However, this method of observation is not possible with those creatures that live mostly out of sight under the tangles of waterweeds or on the muddy floor of a pond.

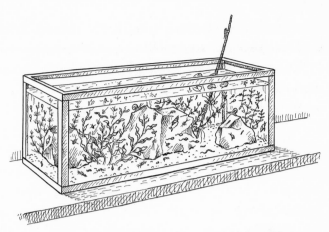

The pond on my windowsill

For the study of freshwater life, therefore, you need an aquarium to help your out-of-door observations. Then the creatures can be observed on their own level through the glass sides, as well as from above. This is the nearest you can get to being down in the water with them.

Your aquarium must be like a real pond. The creatures must have stones under which to hide, and water plants on which to cling and feed. It is important to have floating leaves on which some creatures can rest and air their bodies, and one or two sticks or strong stems rising well out of the water. These will be needed, for example, when dragonflies are ready to break out from their nymphal skins. There must be a fairly large area of water surface, and a gravel bed in which those kinds of creatures that like to burrow can do so. And remember that all the creatures in your aquarium must be of a kind that can live together in a small amount of water.

Collecting stones, water plants, and the creatures themselves for your aquarium will be an exciting outdoor adventure.

The Pond on My Windowsill

1. Setting up the Aquarium

The number of freshwater animals and plants that will thrive together in an aquarium depends, in the first place, on the amount of water it holds. The water should also have plenty of air dissolved in it; otherwise the creatures that breathe through gills would

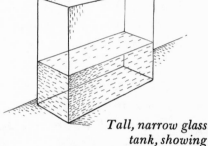

Tall, narrow glass tank, showing correct water level for it

suffocate. Air can only dissolve into the water where the water meets the air—that is, at the surface of the water. This means that you will have to consider carefully what shape aquarium you buy.

The tall narrow type of glass tanks often seen in pet shops are quite unsuitable, for to have enough surface to go with the bulk of water they can only be filled to a shallow depth. The rest is wasted space, and this means that you are always tempted to put in too much volume of water for the amount of surface.

The goldfish bowl type of aquarium is not very suitable either, for the same reason. It bulges out at the middle and narrows toward the top. This means that to have the right extent of surface you must fill the bowl to only a little over half way. So again there is a lot of wasted space and a temptation to put too much water in.

I used to keep a goldfish bowl type of aquarium, however, and I did discover one useful thing about it. The curve of the glass sides caused it to magnify the creatures in the water. This was a real help in observing the smaller creatures, which appeared two or three times their actual size when they moved to the far side of the aquarium.

I now use the type of rectangular aquarium that has an equal width and height. This shape gives enough water surface even when the aquarium is well filled. Mine is eight inches high by eight inches wide by twenty-four inches long. The aquarium has a metal frame and glass sides and bottom, and it looks well on my windowsill. I used to have one that was the same height and width, but shorter, only sixteen inches long. This is a very suitable size but it was

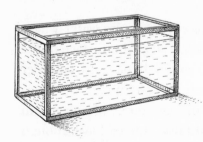

Best kind of aquarium, showing water level

nice to have the extra length of my later one.

The longer or wider an aquarium is, the better; for most swimming creatures spend much more time moving in more or less horizontal directions than up or down. This applies even to surface breathers such as water beetles: they have to swim up at intervals to renew the air bubble that they then carry down with them in the water.

When you have chosen your aquarium, you must then consider making a bed to cover the bottom of it. Some of the water plants will be rooted in this. The beds of natural ponds are usually composed chiefly of fine mud, although the water above this muddy bed is sometimes beautifully clear. The reason is that the large volume of water covering the bed gives ample room for minute impurities to disperse until they become absorbed by plants and tiny scavenging creatures. Some of this water leaks away through outlet streamlets or gradually seeps through places in the banks of the pond. At the same time fresh water trickles in from the surrounding land, and is renewed with every shower of rain. However, mud will not do for the bed of an aquarium, where the volume of water is small and where there is no natural seepage and renewal. Mud would make the water cloudy, and would be continually stirred up by creatures swimming above it and crawling through it. Here, then, you must forsake the rule about making the aquarium look like a natural pond.

I used to use sand, which I washed and rinsed several times to get rid of all impurities before putting it down as a bed for my aquarium. But very soon the droppings of water creatures, the remains of those that died or had been partly eaten, and the decaying leaves and stems of water plants—all these things mixed into the sand and made it first turn gray and finally black. The sand itself held all this dirt and rotting sediment, so that it was very difficult to clean away. It made the water cloudy and impure, and before long the aquarium started to smell.

I now use only gravel, consisting of small stones from about a quarter to a sixteenth of an inch across. The gravel allows the droppings of water creatures and decaying animal and plant sediments to slip down between its stones. This is then easily washed away when I clean out the aquarium. Special aquarium gravel can be bought from any pet shop. If, however, you can get to the seashore, you may be able to collect it yourself from the beach. That is what I did.

I live only a few miles from a pebbly beach, and I discovered that the sea has a very convenient way of sorting out the stones in various sizes along the shore. At the top of the beach the largest pebbles, round or oval and beautifully smooth, were piled up to quite a height. Below these, and stretching along the beach, were medium-sized pebbles. Further down was a shallower strip of small pebbles;

and between this and the sand, which was exposed at low tide, were stretches of gravel.

The stones of the gravel had also been sorted out in sizes by the sea. The larger-stoned gravel was next to the small pebble strip, and the fine gravel was next to the sand, lower down the beach. The stones of the gravel were not smoothly oval or rounded like the pebbles, but more angular and of different shapes. They were beautifully colored, being reddish brown, brown, yellow-brown and bluish gray, with some creamy yellow and some white. I thought what an attractive bed they would make for my aquarium, and I filled a bucket with a collection of stones of the sizes I required.

At home again I emptied half the gravel into a second bucket and then filled both buckets with tap water, leaving them to soak overnight. This was to dissolve away salt from the sea, which would be harmful to freshwater creatures if it remained on the stones. The next morning I poured away the water from both buckets and tipped the gravel from the second bucket back into the first.

Though the gravel had now become free of most of the sea salt, it needed further washing to get rid of the debris from rotting fish, crabs, mussels, and seaweed cast up by the waves. To do this I tipped the amount of gravel I required into a clean bucket half full of water and stirred it vigorously round and round; then poured the swirling water out onto the garden. In this way I washed it in several changes of water until the water poured away was perfectly clear.

With a tablespoon I ladled the clean gravel onto the bottom of my aquarium, to a depth of about one inch.

The next task was to collect three or four largish stones, about the size of my clenched fist, to put on the bed of gravel. I selected stones of different shapes for interest, but all had to have a flat or slightly concave surface on the underside, so that they stood well on the gravel and held down the stems of water plants. After scrubbing the stones under the tap I carefully arranged them in the aquarium.

The stones were placed in the aquarium for four main purposes. They were to help in the artistic "landscaping" of my pond. They would serve as an anchorage for water plants. Their flat or concave undersides would provide shelter from light and safe retreats for some of the water creatures. Lastly the stones would increase the amount of surface over which creatures could crawl or climb, thus giving them a larger area to explore.

When you have laid down the bed and arranged some suitable stones, the next step is to decide on a permanent position for your aquarium. You have to make the decision at this stage because, once the water has been poured in, an aquarium should not be moved. The swirl of water caused by moving can so easily loosen the glass sides from the frame and cause a leak.

You must choose a place where there is plenty of light. This is especially important, as I shall explain later, for the water plants. The place you choose, however, must be out of the direct rays of sunlight. In a natural pond the sunlight can only shine down from the surface, and there are plenty of shady patches and retreats where creatures that do not like it can escape. But direct sunlight, shining through the glass sides of an aquarium, as well as from above, gives an unnatural brightness which is very disturbing to the water creatures. It seems to make them feel exposed and insecure, causing some of them to swim violently about, battering their heads on the glass sides in an effort to escape. Strong sunlight, shining through the glass may also overheat the water, giving discomfort to the inmates. It can damage and even kill the more delicate water creatures.

There are microscopic plants which grow and multiply to a certain extent in an aquarium wherever it is placed; and they form an important source of food for many of the tiny water creatures. But when direct sunlight falls on the aquarium, these plants multiply much too rapidly. At first they make the water only cloudy, but within a few weeks they give it the appearance of pea soup in which nothing can be seen. In direct sunlight too, other kinds of microscopic plants attach themselves to the glass and spread rapidly over the sides of an aquarium, thus obscuring the view from outside.

So if you want to place the aquarium on a windowsill, you must choose one where the window faces north. The only convenient north-facing window in my own house is above the staircase, and it is here that I have my aquarium. If there are no north-facing windows in your house, then your aquarium should be placed on a table close to one of the windows but out of direct sun. Here there will be enough light for the water plants, and fresh air to keep the creatures healthy.

It is important that your aquarium be placed in a cool position—certainly not in a centrally heated room, if possible. Otherwise creatures that become winged adults which leave the water, such as dragonflies and caddisflies, are apt to mistake the season and may emerge in mid-winter. Then, of course, they can find neither food nor mates, and will only freeze to death if set free out of doors. I once made the mistake of keeping an aquarium in a centrally heated room, and this is just what happened.

Having now decided where your aquarium is going to stand, do not put it directly on the surface of the windowsill or table. When a kettle is boiling, when food is being cooked in the kitchen, or when the door of a steaming bathroom is opened, water vapor condenses on the sides of the aquarium. It also condenses on the underside of the aquarium, which is slightly raised from the surface below it by the metal frame. Here the water that condenses cannot easily escape, and after a time it will stain or damage the wood or paintwork. So first put down a cloth mat or a piece of cardboard for the aquarium to stand on.

Now the aquarium is in place and ready for you to pour some water in. Do not disturb the gravel bed

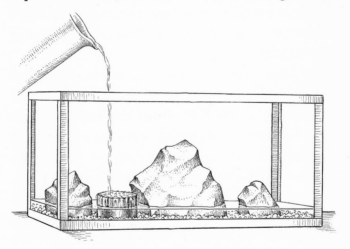

Water being poured into a small tin placed on the gravel

by pouring the water directly onto it, but place a small tin on the gravel and pour the water slowly into this. At the tin overflows, the water will seep down its sides without disarranging the gravel. Continue pouring until the water level has risen to about three inches, then stop and carefully remove the tin. You are not going to fill up the aquarium yet. First you will be going on an expedition to collect some water plants.

2. An Expedition for Water Plants

The equipment you need for collecting water plants is very simple—a few polythene bags to carry the plants home in and a pair of Wellington boots to keep your feet dry. I suggest polythene bags because these are light and less bulky to carry

Wellington boots and a plastic bag

than jars, and as they are waterproof the plants will remain moist and fresh inside them.

Remember to bring a pencil and notebook too.

When you arrive at the pond you have decided on, take a look at its surroundings. Probably there will be some marshy ground beside the pond, and the plants growing on it will be different from those on the dry soil further away. Here, in summer, you may see meadowsweet, greater willow herb, tapering spires of purple loosestrife, and yellow iris. In this region of water-logged soil there will also be smaller plants, such as the water forget-me-not. Water mint is likely to grow here, and in spring you may find clumps of kingcups. The flower buds of

kingcups

kingcups gradually change from green to golden-yellow as they begin to open, and the flowers, which look like giant buttercups, are sometimes two inches across when fully expanded.

Nearer the water's edge there may be sharp-leaved sedges which can cut your legs and hands if you try to scramble through them. Here, perhaps, some willows or alder trees will shade the pond.

The shallow water at the border of the pond may be hidden in places by dense stands of sword-like leaves. The leaves will be either those of reedmace, which in summer bears chocolate-brown cigar-like flower spikes on stems about five feet tall, or those of branched bur reed which has fruit heads like spiky balls, placed one above the other on forking stems. The water plantain also inhabits this shallow region of the pond. Its broad leaves with pointed tips rise out of the water, and in summer they surround a flower stem about two feet high. This bears loose clusters of small three-petaled flowers, pale pink or lilac in color. Where the water's edge is unshaded by taller plants, you may see sprawling clumps of brooklime. Its flowers will show in early summer as little points of deep blue on short spikes between the shiny leaves.

These plants that I have mentioned are some of the typical kinds that you are likely to find growing around ponds and along the borders of slow streams and ditches. They are there because they like to have their feet in the water, so to speak, or because they like marshy soil and cannot thrive where it is dry.

You might find it interesting to make a list in your notebook of the different kinds of plants, with a short description of each. If you do so, group together those growing with their roots in the water, those from the swampy region at the edge of the pond, and

bur-reed and reedmace

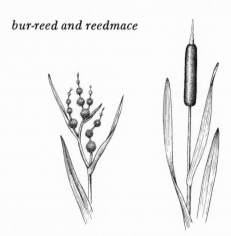

those from the marshy soil further inland. In this way you will discover the particular place, or habitat, that each plant likes.

Now look for plants floating on the surface of the water or growing entirely beneath it. Some of these will be suitable to take home for your aquarium.

If the weather is warm, you may decide to take off your Wellington boots at this stage and paddle. But whether you go into the water with Wellington boots or without them, here is a serious word of warning. **Be sure you choose a pond which you know for certain is fairly shallow throughout; and before putting your feet in the water always test the bottom with a stick.** The floor of ponds is often covered with a layer of fine silt. This may look firm, but when you step on it you sink straight through—perhaps a foot or so down, to the layer of harder soil below. I have sometimes been taken by surprise in this way, and had my shorts soaked with slimy mud, or had my Wellingtons filled with water.

The mud bordering a pond may be treacherous in the same kind of way, especially where it has been churned up by cows coming to drink. Wellington boots can sink in this border mud with a sucking noise and then get firmly stuck. When this happens, the only course is to pull your feet out of the boots, at the risk of tumbling over; then step out into the mud and twist the boots free with your hands. Without the boots restricting the movement of your feet, you can now bend your ankles and pull each foot in turn out from the sucking hold of the mud. So here again it is best to test the muddy edge of a pond with a stick before venturing on it.

You may find the water surface carpeted in places with bright green patches of the common duck-weed. Look closely at these patches and you will see that they are composed of millions of little green discs. Each disc represents a single plant; the common duckweed is, in fact, one of the smallest of our flowering plants. The discs are usually known as fronds. They look like little roundish leaves, but they are really flattened stems, and a very small whitish root hangs from the underside of each.

common duckweed

ivy-leaved duckweed

In late summer a very minute flower may form on the upper surface of some of the fronds. The flower has no petals and consists of two stamens, which carry the yellow pollen sacs, and a tiny pistil, which bears the future seeds. It shows as a yellow speck on the margin of the frond and you can only see it clearly under a good pocket lens.

If you put your finger into the carpet of duck-weed, and bring it out, many of the tiny plants will have stuck to it. You will see that some of the fronds are budding new ones from their margins. These break away to form new plants, and this is how the duckweed spreads over the water.

You may also find the ivy-leaved duckweed floating just beneath the water surface. Its fronds are thin, rather delicate, and pointed at each end. They usually have two smaller fronds growing at right angles from each side. This gives them the appearance of minute ivy leaves.

Common duckweed is not a very good plant for the aquarium, as it soon spreads in a compact mass over the water surface. However, ivy-leaved duckweed is quite suitable. Its delicate translucent fronds, which spread loosely in mid-water, give a nice effect and do not obscure the light.

Another plant to be found floating in ponds is the frogbit. Its round leaves look like miniature water-lily leaves, and in summer it produces delicate white, three-petaled flowers on short upright stems. Its

frogbit in flower

pale roots hang down in the water; and buds at the end of horizontal shoots, known as runners, produce new plants which become detached as the shoots wither. If there is some frogbit floating within your reach, I advise you to take a plant home in one of your polythene bags. In your aquarium its floating leaves will provide useful rafts for any water creatures to climb on. A single plant soon produces daughter plants from horizontal runners.

In late autumn some of these runners, instead of growing horizontally just below the surface, will turn down to the bottom of the aquarium. The buds at their tips do not open, but swell to form green egg-shaped objects, closely covered by protective scales. When the stems wither, the buds become detached, and stand on the floor of the aquarium, remaining there throughout the winter. These are the winter buds, and they contain a store of food to last them till next spring, when they float up to the surface and begin to unfold. The small plant seems in some way to know that winter is coming, and that it must make special provision for its daughter buds. It may be influenced by the shortening day-length and the colder weather. As my aquarium stands against a north window above the stairs, the water in it is soon affected by the temperature outside.

Further out, toward the center of the pond, you may see the large, oval, floating leaves of broad-leaved pondweed. The plant itself does not float but is rooted in the mud. Its small, clustered flowers show as greenish spikes standing upright from the water.

Another plant with floating leaves that is likely to grow in a really big pond is the white waterlily. Its gorgeous flowers float on the water, with their wide, polished leaves spread out around them. The thick, horizontal stem of the white waterlily lies rooted along its length in the muddy floor of the pond, and the long leaf stalks grow upward until they reach the surface, where the tightly rolled leaves unfurl.

The upper surfaces of floating leaves are unwettable. You may see some water that has collected on a few of the big glossy waterlily leaves. Notice that the water does not spread out over the leaves, but beads up into flattened balls like quicksilver. These beads of water get blown or rocked off the leaves with any slight gust of wind, leaving them quite dry. The reason for this is that the leaves have a thin waxy layer on their upper sides to keep the minute, air-breathing pores, called stomata, from getting clogged with water. These stomata are only found on the upper surface of floating leaves. The air they take in fills spaces in the leaf stalks and travels down to the stems and roots in the mud. This helps to buoy up the leaf stalks and also enables the whole plant to breathe.

In the early summer parts of your pond may be covered with the blossoms of water crowfoot, like white-petaled buttercups with golden centers. If you pull up a plant you will notice that the upper leaves which float on the water are roundish with their edges broadly lobed. The underwater leaves, on the other hand, are cut up into fine, almost threadlike segments. These delicate underwater leaves look very attractive in an aquarium, but the

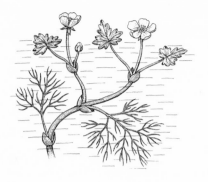

water crowfoot

upper parts of the stem should be cut away from time to time to prevent the floating leaves from covering too much surface.

In the shallower water near the edge of your pond you may see the surface studded with small rosettes of slender leaves. Each rosette looks like a little green star, and these are the upper leaves of starwort. The rest of the plant is submerged. It consists of thin, wiry stems with pairs of slender leaves growing opposite each other and at an angle to those above and below. Only at the top of the stem do the leaves grow close together to form a floating star.

You may like to take a few stems of starwort home for your aquarium. The pale stems and clear green leaves look pretty and let in plenty of light. Starwort grows so well in my aquarium that I have to trim it down frequently, or it would become a tangled mass of twisting stems. Caddisfly larvae help me by biting off short lengths of stem for building their cases.

Look down in the deeper water of the pond and you may see some plants with feathery leaves growing up in clumps from the muddy floor. If you pull a plant up

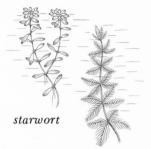

starwort

water milfoil

you will see that the feather-like leaves are arranged in rings or whorls of four along the stem. This plant is water milfoil, and its leaves, like the underwater leaves of water crowfoot, allow the water to flow through them.

Water milfoil is an excellent plant for your aquarium; I always keep some in mine. In the late autumn, when the old leaves begin to wither away, winter buds are formed on the stem. These are shaped like little green cigars. They contain a store of food, and in the following spring they lengthen out and form new plants. These break away from the old stems and soon take root in the gravel.

You are likely to find Canadian pondweed in any pond you visit, as it has become one of our commonest underwater plants. It is easy to recognize, for its trailing stems, rooted in the mud, have small thin leaves arranged in whorls of three. I find Canadian pondweed a useful aquarium plant for, in the daylight, its leaves give out a lot of oxygen. This rises from the plant in little bubbles which aerate the water and help to keep it fresh.

This pondweed was introduced from Canada in about the middle of the nineteenth century. Since then it has spread very fast. Small pieces of stem which break away in the water grow rapidly and take root elsewhere. In some mysterious way fragments of stem must have been transported from one body of water to another throughout the world. No doubt they are sometimes carried on the feet or among the feathers of ducks, moorhens, coots, herons, and other water birds.

You may find some plants in your pond which look rather like water milfoil but are more bushy. If you lift one out of the water you will see that its much divided leaves are arranged in whorls of six along the stem. They are not so fine and feathery as those of water milfoil, and each leaf segment is forked near the tip.

curly pondweed

Canadian pondweed tied to a stone sinker, ready to be buried

The leaves feel rather stiff and horny. This plant is hornwort and it will thrive well in your aquarium, so put a spray in one of your polythene bags. Hornwort is a very hardy plant, and like Canadian pondweed it gives off oxygen freely in a good light. Having no roots to anchor it to the bottom of the pond, hornwort stands freely erect in the water with its stem-bases resting on the mud. Where it grows it often forms dense jungles of vegetation, thus providing shelter for many water creatures.

Curly pondweed, sometimes known as frog's lettuce, is fairly common in ponds. Its crinkled and wavy leaves, about two inches in length, are pale green, translucent, and glossy. I have a spray of this plant in my aquarium: its leaves look very lovely with the light shining through them or glinting from the wave crests of their upper surface. The water snails and caddisfly larvae soon demolish the plant, however, and I have to collect fresh sprays at frequent intervals.

When you have collected enough plants and brought them home, you must next set them out in the aquarium. The plants that will grow up from the gravel should be dealt with first. Floating plants, such as frogbit, can be placed in the aquarium after it has been filled with water. So far, you will remember, the aquarium has only three inches of water covering the gravel.

If you have brought two or more stems of any one

plant, tie them together near the base with strong thread. Then you can either place the base of the stems securely under one of the large stones, or find a small, suitably shaped stone to use as a sinker and tie them firmly to this. A round stone is obviously no use as a sinker, for the thread will not hold onto it. A stone an inch or more long and a quarter to half an inch wide is useful, and if you can find one with a notch in it to take the thread, so much the better. Then bury your sinker with the stem bases under the gravel and let your plant lie in the water.

When you have set out your different plants, using sinkers or large stones to secure them, you can complete the filling of the aquarium with water. Place the small tin back on the gravel and pour water slowly into this. Continue pouring over the tin until the water level is about two inches below the top of the aquarium. Then gently lift out the tin, turning it slowly sideways as it reaches the top of the water and sliding it back and up from the surface. In this way the tin can be removed with hardly a ripple of disturbance. The water plants based on the gravel will now be standing in the water, and any floating plants can be placed on the surface.

I have told you something about the water plants that you are most likely to find in the pond you visit. You may find others that I have not mentioned, and it is interesting to experiment with different kinds for the aquarium. You can choose the plants that look best together. Try arranging two or three kinds to make an interesting contrast in the pattern, size, and color of their leaves and in the growth lines of their stems. Your aquarium can become a pleasure to look at, even before the creatures arrive to add movement to the life already present.

The water plants, however, are not put in the aquarium merely to make it beautiful. They have an important part to play in the whole underwater life. I said in the previous chapter that you should place the aquarium in a good light for the sake of the plants especially. All animals eat ready-made food derived from plants or other animals, but green plants cannot do this. They have to build up their food from water, carbon dioxide, and simple substances dissolved in water, and they can only do this efficiently in a good light. During the process of food building, oxygen is given off by the plants. This dissolves in the water and is breathed in by many water creatures. In return the water creatures breathe out carbon dioxide, which the plants absorb. The plants also breathe in oxygen and breathe out carbon dioxide, but they do so more slowly than the creatures. Thus, in good daylight, the plants give out much more oxygen than they breathe in, and absorb much more carbon dioxide than they would breathe out. Carbon dioxide in more than very tiny quantities would be poisonous to the creatures of the aquarium, and without the plants to remove it they would suffer.

3. An Expedition for Water Creatures

Now all is ready for you to go on an expedition to collect water creatures. Some of these you will find on the surface of the pond, some swimming in the middle depth, some crawling on the bottom, and others hidden in the tangles of waterweed. Not all these creatures are suitable for an aquarium, for various reasons which I shall come to.

You will need a small net of fine, strong mesh with a strong framework fitted to a bamboo or wood

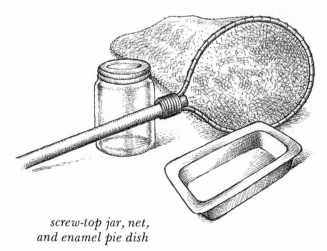

screw-top jar, net,
and enamel pie dish

handle about three feet long. You will, of course, need some screw-top jars to carry the creatures home in. It is a good idea to take a white enamel pie dish too: you can turn out the net into it and the creatures will show up against the white background. A paintbrush and a small wire-mesh coffee strainer are both useful for lifting the creatures from the pie dish into the jars. Very small creatures, such as water fleas, can be poured with the pond water straight from the pie dish to the jars. To do this, slowly drain off the surplus water from the pie dish until there is just a little left in the lower corner. The tiny creatures will have collected here and can then be poured with the remaining water into a jar.

When you arrive at the pond, first stand at its edge and look at the water surface. Here, where the water meets the air, there is an invisible layer known as the surface-film. It is like an extremely fine, elastic skin. When you dip your hand into the water you break this film so easily that you cannot feel that it is there at all. However, certain small and light creatures can run, slide, and even jump on the surface-film without so much as wetting their feet. Others can crawl along the underside of the film in much the same way as a fly walks on the ceiling. There are others that, by clinging to the film, can rest just under the surface of the pond. So this surface-film provides a special habitat for some of the pond creatures.

The first creatures that you notice on the surface-film will probably be the pond skaters. These are narrow, blackish insects just over a third of an inch in length. You see them floating on the surface and jerking themselves over its silvery expanse by vigorous strokes of their long, widespread middle legs.

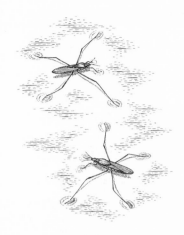

pond skaters

The front pair of legs is short, and points forward. These legs are used for grasping prey, for the pond skater is carnivorous. The back pair is used as twin rudders to steer it on its course.

Pond skaters normally slide or skate over the water surface, but at any alarm they will dart away in a series of leaps. They have good eyesight and are wary and difficult to catch. If you do succeed in netting a pond skater, however, take it gently out of the net and place it on the ground. You will see that it is quite incapable of walking and can only hop about in a hopelessly clumsy fashion. If you carefully hold the pond skater upside down, you will see a coat of minute silvery hairs covering its under-surface. This velvety coating holds the air and acts as a protection against wetting. Pond skaters need a free expanse of water to slide about on, and will not live happily in an aquarium.

Near the edge of the pond and beside a clump of reeds you may see a group of small shiny black beetles twirling about on the surface of the water. Their bodies glitter in the sunshine as they turn and twist about, crossing and re-crossing each other's paths. As they see you approach they dart around

whirligig beetles

in faster and faster curves. Finally, if you come too near them, they dive under the water, each carrying a bubble of air at its hind end. These are whirligig beetles.

Whereas the pond skater lives above the water with only its feet resting on the surface-film, the whirligig beetle adopts a half-in half-out position on the surface. The water falls away from its smooth and highly polished back but the underside and legs are kept immersed and wet. As you watch a whirligig beetle, it appears to be gliding about in some mysterious fashion without legs, though you may notice a series of tiny ripples spreading from its sides. These ripples are caused by the second and third pairs of legs, which are used for swimming. You do not see the legs themselves because they are extremely short and kept in rapid motion as the beetle swims. These tiny swimming legs are broad, flattened and fringed with stiff hairs to grip the water; they are more like little fins than legs. The front legs are of normal shape and are used for grasping prey.

As they scull about on the surface of the pond, the whirligig beetles are able to watch out for attack from above or below the water. Each eye is divided into two parts. The upper portion is above the water surface and for seeing in air. The lower portion is below the surface and for underwater vision.

Between the upper and lower parts of the eyes are the antennae. These short thick antennae float on the surface-film, and the whirligig beetles use them in much the same way as a ship uses its radar instruments. As a beetle swims, little ripples constantly run outward from its body. These are reflected back to the beetle from the shore or any objects on the water. The antennae are highly sensitive to faint movements of the water-film and can detect the reflected ripples. This enables whirligig beetles to avoid bumping into obstacles, including each other, even in the dark.

Whirligig beetles are sociable and gyrate together in close groups. They like to swim in bright sunshine, which they could not get in an aquarium. Nor would an aquarium provide enough water surface for their needs. When I put one in my own aquarium, it constantly struggled to get out through the glass, and whenever I approached the aquarium it dived to the bottom in alarm. So I had to return it to the pond.

The most conspicuous creatures to be found clinging to the underside of the surface-film are the backswimmers. You will see them, usually near the shore, resting upside down and holding on to the surface-film with their first and second pairs of legs, while the hind tip of the body just breaks through the film to allow breathing. Now and again you will see them jerk themselves forward with a few backward sweeps of their long oar-like legs, before coming to rest again.

If you approach too closely, the backswimmers swim rapidly down to the bottom of the pond. Here they hide, holding onto the stems of water plants with their front legs. However, if you keep very still for a minute or two, you will see them, one after another, float underside uppermost, back to the surface again.

Now sweep your net quickly underneath the

backswimmers and you may succeed in catching one or two as they dive. As you withdraw the net from the water you will see them leaping about with powerful kicks of their back legs. Tip them into a pie dish and then transfer one of them to a collecting jar so that you can examine it at close range.

Do not pick up a backswimmer in your hand. Their mouth parts take the form of a piercing and sucking beak. If you hold one in your hand it is liable to give you a painful stab with its beak in self-defense. I know this from experience. Once I saw a backswimmer struggling desperately on the bank of a ditch. When I bent down to investigate, I found that a number of ants were holding

backswimmer resting below the surface film

onto its legs and trying to pull it along. Feeling concern for the fate of the backswimmer, I picked it up and shook the ants off before throwing it back into the water. In return for my kind act, it gave my hand a nasty prick.

When you have transferred a backswimmer to the jar for examination, you will notice how like a boat the shape of its body is, the fawn-colored back, which faces downward in the water, is strongly keeled, while the blackish underside of its body, which faces upward, is flat. On the other hand the yellowish head, with two conspicuous dark eyes, is rounded and blunt, while the hind end, which breaks the surface as the creature rests, is sharply pointed. So the backswimmer differs from a boat in having a blunt prow and a pointed stern. You will notice that the long rowing legs are fringed with hairs, giving them a flat, broadened surface for swimming, while the front and middle legs, which hold to the surface-film, are sharp and curved. These legs are used for gripping prey, for the backswimmer is a fierce carnivore.

backswimmer feeding on a male stickleback

When I was a small boy, and before I knew any better, I put a backswimmer in an aquarium with a pair of sticklebacks. When I went back to look at the aquarium after lunch, I found that the male fish, a beautiful red-throat, was dead and firmly held by the backswimmer, whose beak was embedded in its side. The backswimmer feeds on almost any creature it can capture, so it is not suitable for an aquarium. Return your specimen to the pond after you have examined it.

Adult backswimmers sometimes leave the water and take flight. One even came buzzing into my lighted room on a mild summer evening. As it circled the room I took it for a flying beetle. But when it bumped against the wall, fell to the floor, and started flopping and somersaulting about, I went up to investigate. Then I saw the long rowing legs and boat-shaped body, and realized, to my surprise, what it was. I scooped the backswimmer up on a piece of paper and dropped it out of the open window. It spread its wings and took flight, and I wished it luck in finding its way to the shining surface of some pond.

If you keep your eyes on the pond you are visiting, you are likely to see one or two water snails gliding along the underside of the surface-film from one weedy patch to another.

Look more closely at the water surface around

one of these weedy patches, and you may also notice a small beetle walking upside down across the film. The beetle looks as if it were made of quicksilver, but if you lift it out of the water you will see that it is really black, with a flat undersurface and a shiny convex back. Its underside looks silver in the water because it is covered by a bubble of air. This bubble, which the beetle uses for breathing, is held by a coating of minute hairs. The beetle itself is about a quarter of an inch in length. It is one of the water scavenger beetles and its scientific name is *hydrobius fuscipes*. It will be a useful addition to your aquarium.

Now look down into the open water between the patches of weed. If your pond was visited earlier by breeding frogs or toads, and the season is late spring or early summer, you are sure to see tadpoles swimming to and fro. They are easy to catch in the net, but do not take more than about twenty. When you

toad tadpoles

have netted them, turn your net inside out over the half-filled enamel pie dish and let the tadpoles swim out into the water. Then pour the water with your tadpoles into one of the glass jars and add a spray or two of waterweed. Don't pick up tadpoles with your fingers; they are delicate and easily damaged.

Stand still for a short time by your pond and you may see some small fish, up to one and a half inches long, with grayish-green backs. These are three-spined sticklebacks. The larger ones will be swimming singly to and fro in short jerks, or hovering motionless beside some weed. If you succeed in netting some of the sticklebacks, pour them into a collecting jar to look at. You will notice the three spines on the top of their backs. The spines can be suddenly raised in threat, or made to lie flat. A few of the fish may have greener backs than the others, brilliant blue eyes, and red throats and breasts. These are adult males in breeding dress. The female fish are entirely silver on their undersides.

Each male stickleback in the breeding season has probably built a nest on the floor of the pond from bits of weed that he collected. By making certain swimming movements, he induces several females, in succession, to enter the nest and lay their eggs. The female fish leaves the care of the eggs and newly hatched young to her male partner.

Examine and admire the sticklebacks in your jar, but do not be tempted to take them home. Pour them back into the pond. Sticklebacks, like back-swimmers, are very voracious, and they would soon eat or damage most of the other creatures placed with them in an aquarium.

As you gaze into the open water you will soon notice some smoothly oval beetles swimming about with rapid strokes of their hind legs. These are carnivorous water beetles. Every now and again one of the beetles swims toward the surface and, before reaching it, turns head downward and floats up till it breaks the surface-film with the rear tip of its body. It will remain in this position for a number of seconds to renew its air supply, then swim rapidly down again. Of the larger beetles, the commonest are about half an inch in length, and either black or dark brown with yellowish borders to their wing cases. The more numerous smaller kinds, varying from one tenth to a quarter of an inch, are usually black with red or yellow markings, or else brown.

These fast-swimming beetles can be caught with a rapid sweep of the net when they come to the surface for air. As they are hard, and not easily damaged, you can pick them off the net with your fingers and drop them into a jar. Put some sprays of weed in the jar for the beetles to hold onto. Do not take more than two or three of the larger water beetles, for they feed on other pond creatures. You may take quite a number of the smaller kinds, as they mainly eat minute prey.

Although most of the larger carnivorous water beetles are about half an inch in length, there is one much bigger kind that you may come across. This is the great diving beetle. It measures about an inch and a third in length and is dark greenish-brown above with yellowish borders to its wing cases and thorax.

The great diving beetle is entirely unsuitable for your aquarium, being a fierce and voracious predator which will even attack small fish, newts and young frogs. The larva of the great diving beetle is every bit as voracious as the adult. The larva, sometimes known as the water tiger, reaches a length of over two inches when fully grown. Its narrow, yellowish body, marked into segments, tapers toward

larva of the great diving beetle

the rear, which is tipped with two feathery tail-pieces. Each of the first three body segments bears a pair of shortish legs, and the broad flat head has a pair of curved and very formidable pincers. These are used by the larva for piercing and sucking its prey.

In addition to water beetles, you are almost sure to see some lesser water boatmen swimming in rapid jerks over the pond bottom. They can be distinguished from the beetles by their narrower, more boat-like shape. As you watch these lesser water boatmen you will soon see one of them dart to the top of the water, break the surface-film with its back for a split second to renew its air supply, then dart down again. It acts as if the journey to the surface were fraught with danger, and no doubt it is.

In general outline the lesser water boatman resembles the backswimmer, but its back is flat, and it swims the right side up. There are several kinds varying between a quarter and half an inch in length. All are grayish- or greenish-brown above, minutely streaked with black. Lesser water boatmen are harmless scavengers, so you may safely collect quite a number for the aquarium. Some sweeps of the net over the pond bed and below weedy patches should soon procure all you need. If you pick them from the net, hold them gently, for they are fairly delicate creatures. See that there is some weed in the jar for them to cling to.

Now sweep your net carefully along the bottom of the pond, just skimming the upper layer of mud. When you lift the net up, do not take it out of the water, but swish the base gently to and fro just below the surface. This will get rid of the mud; you will see it coming away through the mesh in brown murky clouds. When these have ceased, your net should be clean. You can then take it up from the water and turn out its contents into the pie dish.

You will notice some cylindrical cases made of tiny sticks, leaf fragments, or small snail shells. These are the cases of caddisfly larvae. If you watch them in the pie dish for a minute, you will see a head and three pairs of legs appear from the front of each case, and the caddisfly larvae will start to crawl about, pulling their cases with them. Pick them up and place them in one of your jars.

caddisfly larva

It is quite likely that you scooped up one or two dragonfly nymphs that were lurking in the mud. These are easily recognized by their roundish heads with large, prominent eyes. They are greenish-brown or mud-colored, and the larger kind grow to about an inch and three quarters long. The shorter and broader kinds, with longish, outwardly sprawling legs are more likely to be taken from the mud, however. They will not hurt you if you pick them up, but do not take more than a couple, for they, too, are voracious predators. Place them in a jar by themselves and return any others to the pond.

You will now find an assortment of smaller creatures left in the pie dish. Among these will be freshwater shrimps and water lice. The freshwater shrimps are curved like a quarter moon, and swim smoothly about or scuttle along on their sides. The water lice look like rather slender, long-legged woodlice. Both these creatures are harmless scavengers. They can be poured with the water from the pie dish into a jar.

You will now be left with a number of creatures sticking to the sides and bottom of the emptied pie dish. There are sure to be water snails among these, some with conical shells, some with flat, coiled shells. There may be one or two leeches clinging to the dish by means of a sucker at each end of their worm-like bodies, and there are likely to be some flatworms looking like small blobs of black jelly.

The snails can be picked up and dropped into a jar, and the delicate flatworms can be lifted on the tip of a paintbrush and shaken off into the water of the jar. Leeches are more difficult to remove, as they cling very tightly with their suckers. A good method is to place a thin stick under the leech's body, then gently but firmly push the stick toward the front end. The leech will then transfer its front sucker to the stick. If the stick is slowly lifted, stretching the leech upward, it will let go of the dish and fix its hind end to the stick. Stick and leech can then be placed in the jar.

Many pond creatures spend much of their lives concealed in the tangles of various waterweeds. In order to collect these creatures, take your pie dish to the edge of the water, then pull up some clumps of weed and rinse them in the dish. Water boatmen and beetles will swim out from the weed, and snails and flatworms will drop off it; so you can take any

more of these that you may need. You should soon
see some other creatures from the waterweed. First,
some small, delicate-looking creatures with slender
antennae, and three feather-
like tailpieces projecting from
the hind tip of their bodies.
You will see them swimming
about in the dish with rapid
flicks of their tails. These are
mayfly nymphs. They may be
taken up in the coffee strainer
or poured with the water from
the dish into a jar.

mayfly nymph

You will also see some larger,
green or yellowish creatures
with wide heads and prominent
eyes; slender, side-spreading
legs, and narrow bodies end-
ing in three leaf-like tailpieces.

damselfly nymph

These are damselfly nymphs. They are more sluggish
than the mayfly nymphs, and they swim with a
sideways wriggling motion. The damselfly nymphs
can be lifted with a paintbrush. Though they are
carnivorous, they feed chiefly on rather small creatures. You could take about half a dozen of these.

You are almost sure to rinse out caddisfly larvae,
mostly smaller than those you found on the mud.
Some will have cases made from green leaves cut
directly from the weed. They would have been

almost impossible to see on the weed itself. Others, with thin green cases, look like bits of stem until you see them moving in the dish. Take what you can find. It will be interesting to have caddis-larvae with various types of cases in your aquarium.

If something that looks like a dead brown leaf, about an inch in length, falls into your dish as you rinse the weed, watch it carefully. It may be a living creature. If so it will soon spread out four slender legs and start swimming in a slow, jerky fashion. At the front of this creature are two thicker, pincer-like legs not used in swimming, and what appears to be the leaf stalk, is a long, tail-like breathing tube. This strange creature is a water scorpion. It is carnivorous and lies in wait for prey, which are grasped in the pincer-like front legs. However, you need have no fear of picking it up. Do not take more than two water scorpions.

Now you should have a good variety of water creatures to take home. When you get there the creatures should not be left in their jars a moment longer than is necessary.

Before releasing the creatures into your aquarium, pour away excess water from each jar, leaving it about a quarter full. A small stick held against the rim of the jar will prevent the water from gushing out: it will trickle down the stick, and any creatures that escape will slide down with the water and can be easily collected. Each jar can then be tilted sideways and gently lowered into the aquarium, thus releasing the creatures without disturbing the water. Rinse any weed sprays in the aquarium water, and remove all creatures left clinging to the jars with a paintbrush or small stick.

In the aquarium all your water creatures should have plenty of room to swim or crawl about, and those liable to be preyed upon have a fair chance of escaping. Of course, some will be caught and eaten from time to time, but this is something you will have to accept. After all, it is something that happens continually in a natural pond. The dragonfly nymphs and water scorpions will take a few tadpoles, mayfly nymphs, and freshwater shrimps, but at least these creatures only lie in wait for the prey to come near enough to be grasped. They will not pursue any that get away. I purposely set a strict limit to the number of larger carnivores, so that the majority of your creatures will be plant eaters and scavengers. This is so in any pond, and should be so in a properly run aquarium.

4. Tadpoles

The best time to go looking for tadpoles is during April or early May. At this time of the year the tadpoles are fairly young and tend to flock together, and so are easy to find. By the end of May or early June they scatter about the pond and lead more solitary lives. By then, too, ducks, moorhens, fishes, dragonfly nymphs, water beetles, and other creatures which feed on them have much reduced their numbers.

Frogs are rather scarce where I live, but toads are plentiful, and in late April I collected about twenty-five to thirty toad tadpoles from a slow stream at the base of the Downs, about a mile from my house. It was easy to know they were toad tadpoles, for they were brownish-black all over, and their tails were slightly rounded at the tip. Frog tadpoles, which are larger for their age, have pointed tails and are dark greenish-gray with a speckling of black and gold spots.

In the aquarium my toad tadpoles spent much of their time clustered in two or three small flocks, scraping the film of minute green plants from the glass sides with their sharp horny jaws. With a pocket lens, I could watch these tiny black jaws opening and closing as they nibbled away.

During the first couple of weeks, the tadpoles spent most of their time scraping at the sides of the aquarium in this way, and as they fed, their tails were kept in constant wriggling

tadpoles eating the green film on the glass

motion. In the early morning, on my way down to breakfast, I would see them all clustered in a dark mass on the glass at the west side of the aquarium. As this was the lightest part of the aquarium at that time, being lit from the eastern sky, I suppose they were trying to warm their small bodies after the night.

Now and again one of the tadpoles would move onto the shell of a water snail that was crawling up the glass, and start nibbling at the surface of its shell. The water snail, however, did not appreciate this at all. It would jerk its shell from side to side in an effort to dislodge the tadpole. Sometimes the tadpole was very persistent, and not easily put off by the snail's maneuver, especially if its shell were coated with green. Then, as a last resort, the snail would let go of the glass, release a bubble of air, and drop to the bottom of the aquarium, causing the tadpole to give up and swim away.

Soon the group of tadpoles was exploring every part of the aquarium. They nibbled their way over the surfaces of large stones and up and down the stems and leaf surfaces of the water plants, eating up the microscopic plants and creatures that were attached to them.

After being in the aquarium for three weeks, my tadpoles had grown considerably, and their bodies had become much more plump and rounded. They now spent more time swimming to and fro in mid-water, and most of their feeding was done at the bottom of the aquarium. With tails waving above them and head downward in an almost vertical position, they nibbled the dirt and debris that lay between the little stones of the gravel bed. This debris was rich in decaying plant and animal material, and the thousands of microscopic creatures living on it gave extra food to the tadpoles. Also, many tiny crustaceans rested here, and though the tadpoles never pursued these creatures when they swam in open water, they probably ate some, as it were by accident, as they nibbled their way through the gravel.

The tadpoles fed voraciously. Their stomachs and intestines must have been kept packed from end to end, as little trailers of waste material were constantly forming at the hind end of the body below the base of their tails.

Occasionally I brought a dead worm in from the

pavement or gutter on wet days. At first the fresh-water shrimps, flatworms, water beetles, snails, and leeches covered the worm before many tadpoles got a chance of feeding. I soon solved this problem. I had made a lid of wire netting for the aquarium to prevent my cat from drinking the water. From this, using a piece of cotton, I hung a section of dead worm, or perhaps a strip of raw meat, in such a way that flatworms, snails, and other crawling creatures could not reach it. Then the tadpoles were able to feed more or less in peace.

Young tadpoles feed entirely on the minute green plants and microscopic creatures that cover the surface of stones and waterweeds, but when they are about half grown they need a diet of meat. I am sure that many aquarium tadpoles die from starvation because their owners are ignorant of this fact. So do remember that it is most important for older tadpoles to be provided with scraps of raw meat or sections of dead worm from time to time. On one occasion in the country, when I was looking for water creatures, I noticed a seething black mass of tadpoles completely covering some object in a ditch. I turned the object over with a long stick and found it was the half-eaten carcass of a dead rabbit. How the poor rabbit met its fate I do not know, but at least it gave hundreds of young toads a good start in life.

When not feeding, my tadpoles were now very

active. It was fascinating to watch the stream of tadpoles constantly swimming to and fro and weaving their way between the stems of water plants. Now and again an individual tadpole would show a sudden spasm of friskiness and dart full tilt from end to end of the aquarium two or three times before coming to rest. Gradually, however, the tadpoles began to spend less time swimming and feeding, and more time resting on the bottom. Several of them stopped feeding altogether and would lie with their heads in the corner of the aquarium, as if they were sickening for something. Little buds had appeared by the base of their tails, and in a few days these developed into perfectly formed hind legs, which gradually lengthened.

At this stage the tadpoles occasionally swam to the surface, their little legs trailing behind them, and pushed their noses above the water before sinking to the bottom again. Their lungs were beginning to develop, and they needed to come up for air. Before this, they had breathed like fishes, by means of gills.

The eyes of the tadpoles had now become larger and more conspicuous. They bulged slightly from the tadpoles' heads, which had grown broader and more distinct from their bodies. Then one morning I noticed a tiny and beautifully formed hand and forearm, just behind the head on one side of the most advanced tadpole. The next day the elbow was showing and a hand had broken through on the

toadlet with hindlegs and forelegs

other side. This tadpole was now not only using its tail to swim to the surface, but also kicking vigorously with its hind legs. A couple of days later its tail had become much shorter and, with less aid from its tail, it had to kick more vigorously to reach the surface for air. It was now a toadlet. As it seemed to be getting exhausted I rescued it with a spoon and placed it in a tin-lid of water, which I had sunk in some damp soil in a deep pudding basin. I covered most of the basin with a sheet of glass to keep the atmosphere damp and prevent the soil from drying.

Meanwhile the other tadpoles were developing—first, hind legs; and then, forelegs; and as their tails began to shorten they found it increasingly difficult to kick their way up to the surface. I rescued another toadlet, and put it in the pudding basin before going off to work, but, when I got home in the evening, one was lying dead at the bottom of the aquarium. It must have become too exhausted to reach the surface for air, and finally drowned.

I realized then that I had to find some way, quickly, of enabling the toadlets to climb out of the water during my absences at work. I had heard or read somewhere that little froglets would climb on to discs of cork floated in the aquarium, when they were ready to leave the water. I therefore cut five discs from a wide cork and floated them in my aquarium. Two more toadlets were now ready to leave the water, and I watched them struggle to climb on the corks. As soon as one of them got its little hands on a cork, the disc drifted away in front of it. The toadlet was unable to get any hold on the cork with its hind legs, and merely kicked its way along the surface pushing the cork in front, until it became tired and gave up. Later, I tried the same experiment with froglets in a school aquarium. They were equally unsuccessful at climbing onto the cork discs.

I had to think out some other way of saving my toadlets. Now I remembered a piece of slate lying under the hedge in my front garden, and brought it in, cleaned it under the tap, and tilted it against the glass in one end of my aquarium. Tilted at an angle of about forty-five degrees, the edge of the slate rested nicely against the top of the aquarium. However, this angle seemed a bit steep for toadlets to rest on, so I pushed the slate down until its upper edge rested against the glass about an inch and a half from the top. Then I took some water out of the aquarium to lower the level, leaving a nice area of slate above the water.

The two toadlets soon discovered the slate and

toadlets climbing up the slate

scrambled up to rest on its surface above the water level. I caught them and put them in the pudding basin. Meanwhile, several other toadlets, not yet quite ready to leave the aquarium, rested on the tilted slate with their heads above the water. Thus I was able to go happily to work the next morning, knowing that the rest of my developing toadlets were safe from drowning.

I am sure that each year great numbers of froglets and toadlets die in their aquaria, simply because their owners do not know how easily they drown if they are not able to climb out of the water when ready to do so. If you have tadpoles in your aquarium, do make sure that you provide them, in good time, with a sloping surface raised above the water.

As the tail of a toadlet grows shorter, its substance is being used to nourish the body; but as soon
as their tails have been absorbed in this way, the
baby toads must start looking for food. At this stage
it is best to take them back and release them at the
edge of the pond or slow stream where, as tadpoles,
they had been collected. However, my baby toads
looked like such delicate little creatures—they were
not much bigger than house flies—that I decided to
try and feed them myself for a short time before
releasing them. Obviously they could eat only very
tiny creatures, and these I had to find in sufficient
numbers for them.

As it was now June, there were plenty of greenfly
clustered on the stems of various plants in the garden. I cut a few of these stems, and with the aid of a
paintbrush, dislodged the greenfly and dropped
them into the pudding basin. At once the little
toads became alert. Each would turn its head to
watch a greenfly crawling on the soil, move stealth-
ily toward it, then with a flash of its tongue too
quick to follow, take it into its mouth—only to put
it out again. Alas, my baby toads did not like
greenfly: and either spat them out or wiped them
from their jaws with their tiny hands. Soon they lost
interest in hunting the greenfly, and would even
move away when one approached.

Next I tried feeding the toads with baby spiders.
There were plenty in the garden and they were easy

to collect. I hopefully dropped about a dozen tiny spiders into the basin from my collecting box—but my hopes were soon dashed. The spiders raced over the soil in the basin, spinning threads from one clump of soil to another, and waggling their minute, curved legs in the air as they let out more thread. Soon they were racing along invisible threads from one squatting toad to another. The baby toads did not like it a bit. They blinked their eyes and wiped spiders from their noses and their hands, or kicked them off their backs with their hind legs, and crouched as low in the soil as they could manage. The spiders were meanwhile hauling themselves up the sides of the basin on their threads. I collected them up and returned them to the garden.

Now I had to think out what baby toads would naturally catch for themselves when they left the water. They could, of course, catch only creatures that lived more or less at ground level. Among the most abundant of ground-living creatures, of a suitable size for baby toads, are tiny wingless insects known as springtails. If you turn up any stone, lift clumps of grass, dead leaves, or the edges of low-growing plants, you will see the springtails leaping about in alarm on the soil you have suddenly exposed.

To collect the springtails I scooped up a few trowel loads of surface soil from under hedges, low-growing plants, stones, and planks of wood in the

ground-living springtail

leaf-feeding springtail

garden, and tipped them straight into a polythene bag. Then I emptied the contents of the polythene bag on a large newspaper spread out on the lawn, and induced the springtails from the soil to jump into a tin. This was done by holding the tin on its side with the open end in front of a springtail while I prodded the soil just behind it. In this way I eventually collected about a dozen springtails and dropped them in the basin. They were just what the baby toads liked and in ten minutes all had been eaten.

I could see that collecting enough ground-living springtails to satisfy the appetites of my baby toads was going to take up every moment of my spare time. Besides, the job was back-breaking. Then I noticed that some tiny yellow leaf-feeding springtails had jumped from the lawn onto the edges of the newspaper. These leaf-feeding springtails suck the juices of grasses and other plants. They have humped, rounded bodies, and look quite different from the narrow-bodied, ground-living kinds. Evidently they were abundant on the lawn, and I thought out a good idea for catching them.

I brought down a piece of white cardboard and a glass test tube from my room, and pushed the white card slowly over a patch of lawn. Sure enough, the yellow springtails were jumping here and there in front of the white cardboard, and several landed on it. I put the glass tube, open end downward, over one of them, and it jumped up to the top and stayed there. Its instinct was to escape upward toward the light. I put the tube over another, and it did the same.

By this method I quickly caught a dozen or so of the yellow springtails and dropped them into the basin. The toads soon licked them up with darting flashes of their tongues. At last I had found an easy way of catching food for my baby toads. By the end of a week they were very plump and had grown noticeably larger. I took them down to the slow stream, where I had caught them as young tadpoles, and set them free on the bank. I had done all I could to give them a good start.

What I have said about the growth and development of my toad tadpoles applies equally to frog tadpoles in most respects. However, in frog tadpoles the lungs develop earlier and they start coming to the surface to gulp air as soon as their hind legs start to appear.

Of course, you may like to visit a pond during early April and collect the spawn of frogs or toads, so that you can watch the development of tadpoles right from the egg. If you do this, however, be sure to break off only a small piece of spawn containing twenty to thirty eggs and leave the rest in the water.

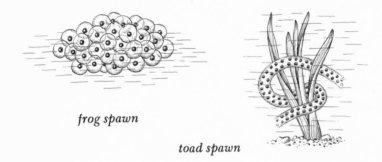

frog spawn

toad spawn

Frog spawn is laid in large masses which float at the surface of shallow water near the edge of ponds. Toad spawn is laid in long strings of jelly, twisted around the stems of water plants well below the surface. The newly hatched tadpoles of frogs and toads are unable to feed, and they cling to the jelly or neighboring stems by means of a sticky sucker under their heads. However, in three days their mouths open and they start feeding on the film of minute plants covering stems and stones. At this stage the little tadpoles look rather attractive, for they have three feathery tufts protruding from each side behind the head. These tufts are their outside gills. A week later the outside gills wither away and a set of inside gills develops below the skin of the throat region. The tadpoles will breathe through these until their lungs have formed.

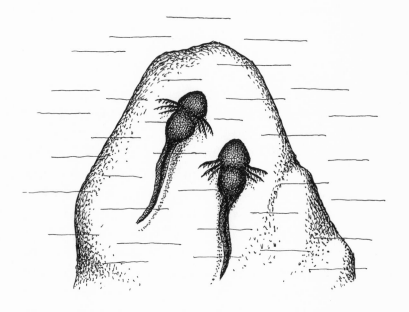

three-day old tadpoles with outside gills

5. Water Snails

The first gentle sweep of your net under a patch of pondweed is almost certain to catch water snails. They are abundant in nearly all ponds and slow streams. Thus you can pick and choose your specimens, sorting out a few of each kind to take for your aquarium. You will soon notice that the snails brought up in your net fall into two main groups. The first group contains snails with more or less conical shells, and the second contains those with disc-shaped shells.

The largest of the snails with conical shells is the great pond snail. Two or three full-grown specimens will be enough for your aquarium.

However, before putting the great pond snails in your aquarium, take one in your fingers and examine the shell. You will see that it ends in a sharp point, which is called the apex. From the apex, the shell makes five turns. Each turn, or whorl, is larger than the one before it, and the last whorl is bigger than all the others put together. This is called the body-whorl, and the others make up what is known as the spire.

As you follow the turns from the apex to the body-whorl, you will see that they coil in a right-handed

great pond snail

spiral. This is the more usual arrangement, but in a few other kinds of snail the shell-whorls turn in a left-handed spiral.

By now the great pond snail has had enough handling, and you will want to watch it moving freely in the aquarium. I never tire of watching this magnificent snail as it glides smoothly and gracefully over the stones and water plants and up the glass sides.

The main part of the body which shows when the great pond snail is extended, is called the foot. The underside of the foot forms a flat suction pad which holds the snail to a surface. Waves of muscle contraction, passed along this pad, cause the snail to move forward. As the snail crawls up the side of the aquarium, you will see that the under-surface of its head is separated from the front of the foot. The upper part of its head, however, continues into the top region of the foot. Notice the flat, triangular tentacles, looking rather like ears, on each side of the head. Unlike the garden snail, the great pond snail cannot draw in its tentacles. They flop down over its head when the snail comes partly out of water, or withdraws into its shell.

When the great pond snail is moving head on toward you, you can see through a pocket lens the two tiny black eyes at the base of its tentacles. Here again this snail differs from the garden snail, whose eyes are at the tips of its tentacles. The eyes of the great pond snail seem to be of little use. When I wave a pencil just in front of a snail, it takes no notice. Its tentacles, however, have an acute sense of touch and the snail seems to rely on these in avoiding objects and finding its way about.

To test whether the great pond snail could even distinguish light from dark, I placed one in a dish, and over it put a cylinder of black paper with an open doorway wide enough for the snail to pass through. The snail took a few minutes to get over the shock of being moved from the aquarium to a dish of water. Then it slowly extended and turned its head toward the door. "Ah," I thought, "it can see the way out." But then the snail turned away and moved off until it touched the black wall of the cylinder. I put it back in the center of the space, and this time the snail's direction took it even further from the opening. It did not appear to see the exit or to know that it was there. Next time I placed the snail nearer the door, and facing it, just to make things easy. It quickly extended, took one look at the open doorway, then turned deliberately around and glided away to the side of the cylinder. It seems likely that the snail had seen the doorway all the time, but did not want to go out into the glare. It preferred the soft gloom inside the cylinder.

On the under-surface of the snail's head is the mouth. When the great pond snail feeds on the green film growing on the side of my aquarium, I like to watch its mouth in action. First the top lip moves up, then the lower lip opens down and side-ways in a wide, pink gape, and a tongue-like organ is pushed out, brushed forward over the glass, and withdrawn as the lips close. The whole action takes about half a second: there is a slightly longer pause, then the mouth opens again. The tongue-like organ is called the radula. It is like a minute strap, studded with rows of micro-scopic teeth. As the radula brushes the surface on which the snail is feeding, the rows of teeth rasp off shreds of food.

The head and foot of the great pond snail are joined by a fleshy column, called the

great pond snail eating the green film on the aquarium glass

neck, to the rest of the body within the shell. This part of the snail's body is permanently fixed to the shell. It contains the heart, stomach, and other important organs, and is partly enclosed in a fold of skin, called the mantle. The rim of the mantle makes the shell substance and builds up the edge of the shell as the snail grows. Thus, if the edge of the shell gets broken, the mantle is able to repair the gap by forming new shell substance in its place. The shell is not just a house in which the snail lives; it is part of the snail itself, just as your fingernail is a part of your finger.

Although the great pond snail lives in water, it has a lung and must come to the surface at intervals to breathe in a fresh supply of air. This shows that its far-off ancestors were land snails. These ancestors gradually took to living in water, but retained the air-breathing lung, and never managed to develop gills.

The lung of the great pond snail is formed by the space between the mantle and the body. A short tube on the right side of the snail leads into the lung. While the snail is under water the mouth of the tube is closed, but when it comes to the surface for air, the tube opens with a distinct *plop*! I can sometimes hear this *plop* from the other side of the room.

When the lung is full of air, the snail is lighter than water, and I occasionally see one rise to the surface simply by letting go of its foothold. On the other hand, if I alarm a snail by trying to pick it off the side of my aquarium, it will expel some air bubbles from its lung and then can drop like a stone to the bottom.

The great pond snail is a hermaphrodite. This means that each snail is both male and female in one. Thus, after mating, each snail of a pair is able to lay eggs. The eggs are laid in a sausage-shaped mass of clear, transparent jelly, attached to a water plant or the glass of the aquarium. The mass contains from thirty to fifty eggs, which look like tiny bubbles. Under a pocket lens, you can see a minute speck inside each transparent egg. This speck develops into a baby snail, which hatches within a few weeks. The shell of the baby snail forms the first tiny whorl of the spire that will develop later as the snail grows.

Great pond snails are very active creatures, and whenever I look in the aquarium I see most of them gliding about or feeding. When I do see one resting, it is usually on the glass at the surface of the water. In this position the snail stays for a short time with its foot half withdrawn into the shell. In winter weather, however, the snails sometimes lie up for a day or two in the gravel at the bottom of the aquarium.

Great pond snails eat an enormous amount, and in winter when there is not much in the way of water plants, I help them with a few pieces of potato peel every week. I also give them lettuce leaves and bits of cabbage, and in summer I occasionally put a strip of cucumber peel in the aquarium. The snails are particularly fond of this. They also like animal matter, and feed readily on bits of cooked meat and dead worms that I drop into the aquarium from time to time.

Closely related to the great pond snail is the wandering snail. This is by far the most abundant of all freshwater snails, and can be found in almost all stretches of still or slow-flowing water. I have found wandering snails in children's boat ponds, fountain bases, and garden pools, as well as in lakes, wide rivers, and ditches.

The wandering snail is smaller than the great pond snail, with a shell from half to three quarters of an inch long when full grown. Its shell differs from that of the great pond snail in having an extremely small spire and a large, rounded body-whorl. Apart from its shell, however, the wandering snail looks like a smaller edition of the great pond snail, but with shorter and more ear-like tentacles.

Another common pond snail with a conical shell is the bladder snail. This is a fairly small snail with a shell just under half an inch long when full grown. The spire is short, with coils turning to the left, and the polished, oval body-whorl has a golden sheen over its brown color. This gives the snail an attractive look in the aquarium.

The bladder snail has slender tentacles, and the eyes, like those of other pond snails, are at their base. The foot is narrow, with a long tail, which tapers to a point. This gives the bladder snail a rather racy appearance as it glides along. It is, in fact, an active and rather fast-moving little snail.

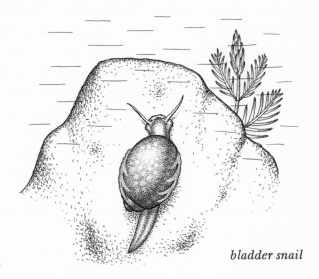

bladder snail

The bladder snail is easily irritated. When touched by a passing snail or other creature, it jerks its shell violently from side to side. If a freshwater shrimp or water beetle alights on it, the bladder snail swings its shell almost full circle in attempting to dislodge the intruder. In doing this, the snail lifts its shell high up on the slender neck, which I almost expect to see twist in half. Several times I have watched a great pond snail and bladder snail meet on the side of my aquarium. Each time, as the great pond snail began to crawl over it, the bladder snail swung its shell so violently that it leapt backward off the side and was propelled through the water for an inch or two before falling.

When I examine a bladder snail through my pocket lens, I can see that its brown shell is dappled with light yellow spots. I can also see a number of thin, grayish objects clinging to the shell, as if it were being clutched from below by a many-fingered hand. These are extensions of the mantle, which curves out over the rim of the shell. It has been suggested that they act rather like a gill, so that the snail can stay a long time under water. However, the bladder snail has a lung, which opens on the left of its body. I have often seen the snail come up for air, and the bubble in its lung shows through the delicate shell as a shining goldish patch.

Sometimes I see a bladder snail letting itself down from a water plant on a fine thread of slime, in much the same way as a spider will descend on a thread of silk. I cannot actually see the thread in the water, but can tell that the snail is suspended and not falling. On two occasions, as I watched a bladder snail hanging by its invisible slime-thread from a leaf, it turned around and climbed up the thread and on to the leaf again.

Now we come to the snails which have disc-like shells coiled in a flat spiral. The largest of these is the great ramshorn snail. This is quite a common water snail and its shell measures an inch or more across when full grown. The shell is dark brown, and about a quarter of an inch thick. Its coils widen fairly rapidly from the center to the rounded opening. I like to keep this large snail in my aquarium as it makes a fine contrast in shape to the great pond snail.

great ramshorn snail

The head and foot of the great ramshorn snail are dark reddish-gray and the tentacles are long and slender. These are placed well back on its head, giving the snail a somewhat long-faced appearance. The opening of the lung, like that of the bladder snail, is on the left, and in front of it an extension of the mantle protrudes below the shell. This is well supplied with blood and is believed to act as a kind of gill. Certainly the great ramshorn does not come up for air as often as the great pond snail.

When the great ramshorn lays its eggs on the side of the aquarium, the clear jelly containing them

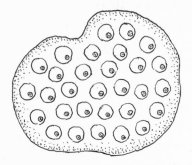

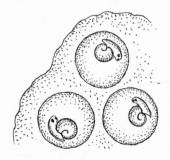

*eggs of the great ramshorn
snail on the aquarium glass*

*baby ramshorn snails
moving inside their eggs*

is curved in a more or less circular shape. One of my snails, however, laid its eggs on a plant stem, and then the mass was in the form of a cylinder enclosing the stem. The eggs themselves are pinkish and transparent, and the mass of jelly usually contains about thirty. When the baby snails have taken form in the eggs, they are very pale in color, and under a pocket lens their black eyes show up sharply. They hatch in about three weeks, but for a day or so before hatching, the little snails become quite active. At this stage I have watched them, through my pocket lens, gliding round and round inside their eggs.

There are several kinds of smaller ramshorn snails which have extremely flat shells with many narrow coils. A very common one in the ponds I visit is the whirlpool ramshorn. Its shell is about a third of an inch across and looks like a little coiled watch-spring. The opening to its shell is very small, and the snail itself has what seems a ridiculously tiny foot, only an eighth of an inch long and oval in shape. With this small foot, the whirlpool rams-horn can only creep along at an extremely slow pace. The foot is dull red, and the delicate, thread-like tentacles are pink.

I have described some of the snails of the two different groups you will have been collecting—those with conical shells and those with disc-like shells. However, I have kept one of the conical-shelled snails until last, because it differs greatly from the other snails of both these groups. This snail is the common bithynia.

All the snails I have talked about so far have lungs, and are descended from land snails. The common bithynia has no lung. It breathes under

common bithynia

water by means of a plume-like gill under its mantle opening, and its ancestors have always been water snails. Another difference is that whereas the lung-breathing snails are hermaphrodite, a bithynia must be either male or female, not both.

The common bithynia has a dark brown, evenly conical shell, half an inch long when full grown. If you pick one up from your net and hold it upside down, you will see that the mouth of the shell is closed by a neatly fitting door of hard material. This door, which protects the snail in its shell, is called the operculum. It is attached to the upper surface of the foot at the tail end. When the bithynia has withdrawn into its shell it closes the door by curling its tail over and forward.

The common bithynia is very slow moving. The front of its foot is flat and square and the tail end rounded. The eyes are at the base of its long, thin tentacles and on their outer side; those of lung-breathing water snails are on the inner side. The head of the bithynia is held rather high above the foot, and it curves down and forward to form a trunk-like snout. The mouth, at the base of the snout, is an upright slit formed by two side lips. I noticed that when the bithynia scraped some green film from my aquarium, the radula was brushed backward over the glass; in the lung-breathing snails it brushes forward.

The head and foot of the common bithynia appear dull blackish-gray—or so I thought until I saw one under my pocket lens. The lens then revealed that the dark skin of its upper side, head, and tentacles, was striped and flecked with shining gold. I was so fascinated by the strange beauty of the common bithynia, that I could hardly take my eyes from the lens. With its gold striped tentacles waving slowly to and fro, up and down, its black eye gazing sideways, and its sensitive, probing snout, it looked like some dark-skinned, gentle monster that had been decorated for fun with strips and patches of goldleaf.

One evening I watched a female bithynia laying her eggs on the side of aquarium. She had already laid about twenty-five when I started watching. The eggs were tiny transparent globules arranged in a neat double row facing downward. The mother snail squatted on the end of the double row of eggs with the front part of her foot protruding beyond them. The eggs were laid singly at four or five minute intervals. Each egg, as it was being laid, came out from between the front edge of the foot and the underside of the snail's head, and it slid smoothly backward under the foot to join the end of the double row. The egg always slid into its correct

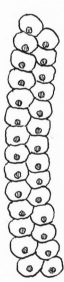

eggs of bithynia
on the aquarium

position, either on the left or right of the last egg laid, so that the numbers in the two columns were kept equal. It seemed to move of its own accord, but no doubt it was guided into place by the muscles of the mother snail's foot. When the mother snail finally moved away, she had laid thirty-two eggs.

Under my pocket lens I could see a golden-brown speck in each transparent egg. These specks should have developed into baby bithynia snails, but they never did—for the next day a great pond snail came along and ate them all up.

6. Caddisflies

If you look down into the water of the pond you visit you are almost certain to see some caddisfly larvae dragging their cases of stem fragments over the muddy bottom. Others will be clinging to the clumps of waterweed that you pull out with your hands, or on the floating weed that you bring up in the net. But you will have to search very carefully for these caddis-larvae. Their cases of plant material not only protect the soft bodies of the larvae, but serve as a wonderful camouflage.

There are many kinds of caddis-larvae. Each kind chooses a particular material for building its case, and arranges it in a special pattern. Thus you can usually tell the kind of caddis-larva by looking at its case alone.

Most of the caddis-larvae that I dredge from the bottom of the pond have cases made from bits of plant stem placed crosswise on the case. This gives them a very spiky appearance. Others have cases made entirely from small snail shells. The kinds that I find on the water plants near the surface have more slender cases made from pieces of leaf and stem placed lengthwise.

However, if the materials that the caddis-larvae naturally choose are not present, they build cases from what is at hand, if given enough variety. For example, there are very few bits of stem on the floor of my aquarium, and so the caddis-larvae that had built from loose stem fragments now began to fix

caddisfly larva

small gravel stones to their cases. As they always build forward, these larvae soon had the front half of their cases patterned with little stones of different shapes and colors. This made an interesting contrast with the criss-crossing stems that now formed only the hind part of their cases.

The caddis-larvae with cases of small shells used the snail shells in my aquarium. They did not mind whether the shells they used contained living snails or not. Thus some of my little snails ended their lives cemented together, like bricks on a round chimney.

Other caddis-larvae, seeking material for enlarging their cases, used their jaws to cut out pieces of leaf and stem from plants growing in my aquarium. Some of the larvae always cut one or two pieces of stem about twice the length of their cases, and fixed these so that they extended backward, like long, stiff tails. These tail pieces often hampered the larvae by getting caught up in

caddisfly larva with long tail-stem

the plants of the aquarium. However, in a pond they would probably give an added protection to a caddis-larva by making its case more difficult for a moorhen or a hungry fish to swallow.

You only see the front part of a caddis-larva extending from its case as it moves about in the aquarium. This looks very like the front part of a caterpillar. But whereas the caterpillar's three pairs of legs behind its head are short, the caddis-larva's second and third pair are fairly long. These second and third pairs are used for crawling or climbing plant stems. The short first pair, however, is used for holding particles of building matter, which the larva fixes with silk from its mouth to the front edge of its case.

The silk comes out of the caddis-larva's mouth

as a sticky liquid. This glues the pieces of case material together and quickly hardens. The silk is also used to line the inside of the larva's case. I have occasionally removed a caddis-larva from a rough or bristly case, and slit the case open with a pair of scissors. Each time I found that, in contrast with its outer surface, the inside of the case was smooth and silky.

It is not difficult to remove a caddisfly larva from its case, but you must hold the case very carefully, for it is quite fragile and easily crushed. What I do is to hold the case lightly between the thumb and forefinger of my left hand while I push a narrow stem gently into the hole at the back of the case. The larva does not like to have the sensitive rear portion of its body touched, so it crawls out from the front of the case with its rear end tucked underneath— like a nervous dog creeping away with its tail between its legs. I then drop the naked larva into a saucer of water, so that I can examine it.

Without its case, the caddis-larva looks a very defenseless creature. Its head and the front part of its body, which bears the legs, are brown, with a horny skin. The hind body, normally kept within the case, is soft and yellowish-white. When I look at the hind body under a pocket lens, I can see two rows of thread-like filaments along its sides and bending over the back. These are the gills, for the caddis-larva breathes under water. The hind body ends in two sharp, forward-curving hooks. These grip the silk lining at the base of its case and hold the caddis-larva firmly in. For this reason you must never try to pull a caddis-larva out from the front of its case. It will resist your efforts by hooking itself more firmly in the case; and you would injure the larva, or even tear it apart, if you went on pulling.

As the naked caddis-larva rests on the bottom of the saucer, it

caddisfly larva without its case

waves its hind body up and down with a steady rhythm. This waving motion of the hind body continues when the caddis-larva is in its case. At the beginning of the larva's hind body there are three fleshy lumps, one on top and one at each side. The lumps hold the larva centrally in the case, leaving room for water to pass between them. A current of water, caused by the rhythmic movement of the larva's hind body, enters the front of the case and leaves through the hole at the back. In this way the larva keeps its gills supplied with fresh water while remaining in its case. Sometimes a caddis-larva with a case of thin leaves shows up against the bright daylight, as it clings to a stem near the surface of my aquarium. Then I can just see the shadowy movements of its hind body through the pale green of its case.

On one occasion, after removing a caddis-larva from its case, I put the empty case in the saucer with the larva. Then I waited to see what the larva would do. It crawled around the saucer until it reached the empty case. As soon as it touched the case it became interested, and clambered all around and over it, from one end to the other and back. After about two minutes of carefully examining the case by prodding it with its mouth and front legs, the larva finally moved in. It entered through the hole at the back of the case, and a few seconds later poked its head out at the front. It twisted its head over and round the opening to examine the front of the case with its mouth and forelegs. Then, satisfied that all was well, it hooked itself firmly in and started to crawl around the saucer. I picked it up and restored it to the aquarium.

I removed another caddis-larva from its case and dropped it into the saucer. Then I gave it back its own case to see if it would behave in the same way. This second larva was much more cautious, and examined its case for fifteen minutes before moving in. It entered the case at the front opening and pushed its head out through the narrower hole at the rear. Now the caddis-larva started to crawl across the saucer with its case on back to front. I put it back in the aquarium.

I thought it would be fun to see if the caddis-larvae would build themselves cases of really bright material, so that I could use them to decorate the aquarium. I collected pieces of gold and silver paper and the colored metallic papers from chocolate candies. When I had a good selection of these I cut them into small fragments and scattered them in a saucer of water. I then removed two caddis-larvae from their cases and put them among the glittering fragments. The caddis-larvae wandered around the saucer, looking for something to cover their nakedness. Now and again one of the larvae would pick up a fragment, turn it over and examine it, then drop it and move on. They did not seem to like the feel of the metal paper. However, after half an hour, one of the larvae had fixed a few pieces very loosely around the front of its body. I waited another half hour, but it made no attempt to dress itself further, or even to handle any more fragments. The other larva was still naked.

As this silver paper experiment was not a success, I cut up bits of colored paper from magazines, and placed these in another saucer of water. Then I put the two caddis-larvae among them. They immediately showed an interest in this softer paper and started picking up pieces and feeling them with their mouths. An hour later they had both made little collars of colored paper and were fixing more bits in front of these. I noticed that the caddis-larvae did not select any particular colors. Their paper collars were made from a fair sample of the different colors in the saucer.

It was now time for me to go to bed, so I moved the larvae and the colored fragments into a small dish with more water, and left them overnight. The next morning both the larvae were loosely dressed in paper fragments. With little colored streamers waving around them as they crawled about, they looked as if they were about to take part in some underwater carnival.

I now put the two caddis-larvae back in the aquarium. Here they started to pick up bits of gravel from the aquarium floor, and had soon built circles of little stones in front of their paper dresses. In a couple of days each larva had a new gravel case with two or three colored strips of paper at the back.

I did not throw away the metallic paper fragments that had been scorned by the two larvae. Instead, I scattered them on the floor of the aquarium to see if any other larvae would make use of them. To my surprise, a week later several of the caddis-larvae had glittering patches of metallic color on their cases. Encouraged by this, I cut up more wrappings from chocolate candies—the gayest I could find—and dropped the pieces into the aquarium. The caddis-larvae were quite willing to mix these among the stems, leaves, and gravel stones they used for building. It was not long before many of them sparkled with points of silver, gold, red, violet, green, and blue, as they crawled over the gravel, clambered up the stones, or climbed the stems in my aquarium.

I have not yet mentioned the swimming caddis-larva. This is a very dainty creature with a long, slender case, tapering almost to a point at the back. The case is made entirely from small pieces of leaf, all cut in neat ellipses and carefully arranged in rows

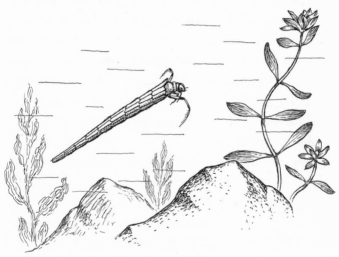

the swimming caddisfly larva

that spiral forward. The swimming caddis-larva feeds on the leaves of water plants, and as it swims from one clump to another, it looks like a piece of green stem propelling itself through the water. The larva uses its long, feathery hind pair of legs to swim with. These swimming legs curve right over the larva's head when it is resting on a leaf or stem. I particularly like to watch this charming little caddis-larva as it glides to and fro, like an animated stem, through the mid-water of my aquarium.

Most caddis-larvae feed on the same kind of varied materials as water snails. Like caterpillars, they have strong jaws, and they nibble their way through the leaves of water plants. They also like pieces of lettuce, cabbage, potato-peel, and cucumber rind, as well as an occasional dead worm or morsel of cooked meat. When fully grown, the larvae cease feeding and attach their cases, with silk, to a solid surface. My larvae fixed themselves to the large stones in the aquarium. Here they closed each end of their cases with a network of silk and changed into pupae.

The pupa of the caddisfly is something like that of a moth; but whereas the moth-pupa has a hard, firm skin, the caddis-pupa is rather soft and delicate. It also differs from the moth-pupa in having its legs and antennae free, instead of their being fixed to the body; and, as it must continue breathing under water, there are gill-threads on its hind body.

The caddis-pupa remains fixed to its stone for two or three weeks. Then, when it is ready to change into an adult caddisfly, the pupa becomes active. There is a pair of strong jaws on the pupa's head, and with these it bites its way out of the case. The jaws of the pupa are only used on this one occasion, and have been developed specially for this single action.

The first and second legs of the pupa are capable of free movement. The second pair are long, and feathered with stiff hairs toward the tip. As soon as the pupa has pulled itself out of its case, it uses these oar-like middle legs to row itself up to the surface. It climbs out of the water up a reed or stem, or onto a floating leaf. In a few minutes the pupal skin splits and the adult caddisfly emerges.

Occasionally I have been present when a caddis-pupa has just come out of its case and is swimming in the aquarium. Then I lift it out with a spoon and place it on the table, so that I can watch it closely. For a minute or two the pupa walks here and there over the tablecloth, then settles. It remains perfectly still for about five minutes, then starts to lengthen and draw in its hind body with a pumping motion. Suddenly, it straightens its legs, lifting the front of its body from the table. It seems to be pushing and straining upward, while its claws grip the table-cloth. Then a slit appears just behind the head and along the top of its mid-body, or thorax, to give it its proper name. The slit opens sideways and the head and thorax of the emerging caddisfly push upward and come free. The first and second legs are quickly pulled out from their pupal sheaths and come down to grip the surface of the cloth. Now the caddisfly can pull forward. As it does so the long antennae slide out from their back-pointing sheaths, the third legs and wings come free, and with a final lurch, the hind body, or abdomen, is released. The adult insect takes a few shaky steps from its crumpled pupal skin and rests from its exertions.

The forewings of the newly emerged caddisfly are silvery-green, but in a few hours they change to brown with some darker and lighter markings. As it rests, with its long, rather narrow forewings placed roof-like over its back, the caddisfly looks very like

caddisfly

a moth. Unlike a moth, however, it rests with its long antennae pointing forward—a moth rests with its antennae turned back beneath its wings.

Most caddisflies fly at night, and in summer they often come into my lighted room, although my house is a good half-mile from the nearest pond that I know of.

Adult caddisflies live only for a week or two. They have no biting jaws, but have been seen sipping the dew from leaves. I have discovered that those from my aquarium like sweet juices. When they have emerged, I keep them in a jar and let them free after dark. Before releasing them, I give them some dilute black-currant juice on a wad of cotton wool, to nourish them before their journey. One of the caddisflies stayed for an hour and a half, sipping the juice from its cotton-wool pad, before flying off into the night.

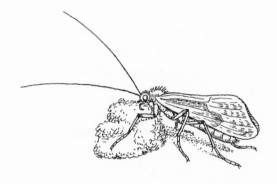

caddisfly drinking fruit juice from a wad of cotton wool

7. Dragonflies and Damselflies

A caddisfly has a young, underwater form called a larva, very different from the adult form; and, as a between stage before becoming adult, there is a resting form called a pupa. In dragonflies the development is quite different. The young, underwater form, called a nymph, is much more like the adult form, and there is no resting stage between the two. The change from nymph to adult dragonfly is gradual but continuous. Wing buds, for example, form early in life and become larger as the creature grows. Finally, the nymph climbs out of the water, splits its skin, and the adult dragonfly emerges.

The young of all insects which have this sort of life history, in which there is no pupal stage, are known as nymphs.

Dragonfly nymphs are dingily colored creatures —dull brown, greenish brown, or yellowish gray, often mottled with darker patches. Thus they are very difficult to see in the pond. It would never do for them to be gaudily colored like the adult dragonflies, for they must be unnoticed as they approach their prey or wait for it to come within grasping range.

The head of a dragonfly nymph is very like that of the adult insect. It is broad and somewhat rounded, with two large eyes that bulge out on either side, and a pair of short, bristle-like antennae in front. The thorax, except in very young nymphs, is covered by four scale-like wing buds which point backward over the front of the ab- domen. It bears three pairs of well-devel- oped legs, used for walking and for cling- ing to stems or stones.

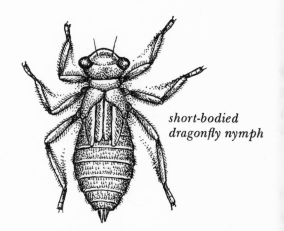

short-bodied dragonfly nymph

The splayed out legs of the broad, short-bodied types of dragonfly nymph help to keep them from sinking in the mud as they rest on the bed of a pond. The abdomen, which in the longer-bodied dragonfly nymphs is somewhat cigar shaped, ends in three short, spine-like tail pieces.

When a dragonfly nymph is resting parallel to the front of my aquarium, I can see the underside of its abdomen moving up and down with a regular pulsation. This is the breathing movement of the nymph as water is drawn in and then expelled through the hind opening of its body. The back end of the nymph's gut, or food canal, is broadened out into a special breathing chamber which is lined with thread-like gills.

To observe the flow of water from this breathing chamber, I once placed a nymph in a saucer with just enough water to cover it. Every three seconds or so a ripple passed over the surface from the tip of the nymph's abdomen as the water was breathed out.

When I moved my hand forward to pick up the dragonfly nymph, it shot a jet of water from the tip of its abdomen into the air, splashing the table about six inches from the saucer. As I picked up the nymph, another jet splashed my arm, and when I put it back in the aquarium, it darted through the water in a series of jerks. As the nymph swam, its legs were pressed against its body, which remained stiff, yet the leaves of the aquarium plants were shaken by a movement of water as it jerked past them.

After swimming around the aquarium, the dragonfly nymph spread out its legs and landed on the bottom. I then reached down and touched it lightly with the tip of a pencil. At once the nymph darted up and forward, leaving behind it a puff of silt and debris above the gravel. It was easy to see that the nymph swam by shooting out jets of water from its breathing chamber.

dragonfly nymph swimming up from the bottom

The dragonfly nymph is, indeed, a wonderfully designed creature, able to breathe through the hind opening of its body and to use its breathing apparatus to swim with. When the nymph squirted on to the table as I moved to lift it from the saucer, it was simply trying to swim away by its method of jet propulsion.

The dragonfly nymphs in my aquarium, however, spend very little of their time in swimming, unless alarmed or suddenly disturbed by something. Mostly they lurk motionless on the gravel or on a plant stem or upright stick. When they do move, they usually crawl very slowly down a stem or over the bottom, and soon come to rest in the new position. You may wonder how they ever manage to catch the more active creatures that form their food.

The jaws of insects move sideways, not up and

head of dragonfly nymph showing mask folded and extended

down like ours. These jaws are supported from below by a kind of firm lower lip. In dragonfly nymphs this lower lip has been specially developed for catching prey at a short distance. It has become greatly lengthened and has an elbow-like joint in the middle, and a pair of pincer-like claws at the tip. At rest, this prey-catching limb is folded under the head so that the elbow points backward between the nymph's front legs. In this position the broad, front part of the limb, tipped with folded pincer-claws, covers the nymph's mouth and lower face. Hence, this food-catching apparatus in dragonfly nymphs is known as the mask.

When a small creature swims or crawls within striking range of a lurking nymph, this mask is shot forward with lightning rapidity. The pincer-like claws grip the prey, and the mask folds back, bringing it to the nymph's mouth. Now the nymph grips the prey in its true jaws, chews it up and swallows it.

Try to imagine that you have a single, forward-moving arm fixed under your chin, so that the elbow rests against the front of your chest and the hand covers your mouth. If you wanted to reach for food you would first turn to face it, then extend your arm, grasp the food in your hand and bring it to your mouth by folding your arm again. Your arm would then have moved in the same way as a nymph's mask when it captures prey.

Hour after hour two dragonfly nymphs crouch motionless in my aquarium. They wait, with all the patience of spiders at the edge of their webs, relying on stillness and their drab colors to conceal them from an approaching prey. With almost equal patience I sit watching them.

Once I saw a freshwater shrimp swim in a neat arc from one end of the aquarium and alight on the big stone to which one of my nymphs was clinging. For a minute it nibbled at some debris on the top of the stone, then it shuffled on its side over the stone toward the waiting nymph. Again the freshwater shrimp stopped and nibbled at the stone surface. It was now about an inch from the nymph, and on its right. The dragonfly nymph turned its head, and with extreme caution, revolved its body so that it faced the shrimp. Then, with the controlled slowness of a chameleon, it moved its legs, one pace, two paces forward. The shrimp finished nibbling and started to move away, but before it had gone a millimeter the nymph's mask flashed out. An instant later the freshwater shrimp was crushed between

dragonfly nymph stalking a freshwater shrimp

strong jaws in the dragonfly nymph's mouth.

On another occasion as I sat watching, a lesser water boatman swam down to the bottom of the aquarium and alighted just out of range of a dragonfly nymph. The nymph at once turned to face it. Twice the water boatman gave a backward flip with its hind legs, and each time the nymph moved up to within striking range. Then the water boatman became perfectly still, resting as it clung to the gravel with its middle legs. It seemed an easy prey. All the dragonfly nymph had to do was to flip out its mask and take it. I waited, but the nymph made no attempt to catch the water boatman. Ten minutes passed. Then the dragonfly nymph slowly turned away and moved to a new position. The absolute stillness of the water boatman seemed to baffle the nymph; and apparently the nymph could not smell its prey. It looked as if dragonfly nymphs hunt by sight alone and only recognize a prey by movement.

I noticed a disturbance in the aquarium one afternoon and saw that a dragonfly nymph was clinging head downward to an upright stick and wagging its abdomen violently from side to side. Then I noticed that the larger nymph, which usually occupies the stick, was clinging head upward with its face about a third of an inch below that of the smaller one. As I watched, the smaller nymph struck out with its mask at the face of the larger nymph. The latter started retreating backward down the stick, pursued by the smaller nymph, which continued to strike at it. When the larger nymph reached the bottom of the stick and its abdomen touched the gravel, it seemed suddenly to wake up, and then lashed back with its mask at the smaller one. Both nymphs now lashed at each other's faces, at the same time wagging and rotating their abdomens in what looked like a display of angry threat. After a few minutes of this, the tables were turned, and the smaller nymph started to retreat backward, then turned round and ran up the stick pursued by the larger one. On reaching the surface, the smaller nymph climbed out onto a floating leaf of frogbit and moved off down the stem, while the larger nymph clung, victorious, to the stick.

A week later I noticed that the smaller dragonfly nymph seemed to have grown. It was now almost the size of the larger one. It had grown suddenly, in the space of an hour. When I first looked, I thought the two nymphs were standing on the gravel, until

dragonfly nymph and newly moulted skin

I saw that the larger one was clinging, as usual, to its stick. Then I realized what had happened. The smaller nymph had moulted its skin, which was also standing on the gravel, behind it. The skin still held its shape, and looked like another, slightly unsubstantial nymph.

After emerging from its old skin, the body of the dragonfly nymph had expanded rapidly. The nymph had puffed itself up as much as possible while its new skin was still soft and flexible, in order to leave space for some growth to continue when the skin hardened. A few hours later the skin had set, like a thin coat of mail, preventing any further growth in size Now the dragonfly nymph was strong and firm enough to move away. It went to its watching post on the big stone and waited the approach of its next meal.

In August the larger dragonfly nymph climbed out of the water and up the dry portion of the stick. It climbed the stick in the darkness of night and rested an inch from the top. Some hours later, when the rising sun had brightened the sky outside the window, and I was up and watching, the skin of the nymph split, first along the top of its thorax, then down across the head. Slowly the slit widened and a lump pushed upward forcing the split skin out on either side. There was another upward lunge and

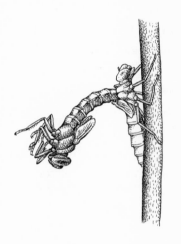

dragonfly emerging from the nymphal case

then the pale brown head and thorax of the dragonfly appeared. Now the dragonfly seemed to grow outward from the split thorax of the nymph. Its small wings were drawn out from the skin of the wing buds, and after a few twitches its leg came free. The dragonfly's head and thorax then turned backward so that the folded legs were pointing up. Slowly its long, limp abdomen pushed out from the nymphal skin and curved, back downward, in an arc. Finally the dragonfly came to rest, hanging head down with only the end part of its abdomen still held within the skin. For several minutes, while I waited, the dragonfly hung motionless in this position. I returned to my bedroom and got dressed.

Ten minutes, twenty minutes, half an hour later, the dragonfly was still hanging motionless in the same position. Fortified by breakfast and a few cups of tea, I had set myself again to watch and wait. Soon the dragonfly twitched its legs. Then it gave an upward lurch, but fell back in the old position. A minute or two went by and again it gave an upward lurch, but fell back. I was worried. Perhaps the dragonfly was too feeble to continue its emergence. Very gently I placed a finger under its thorax and curved it upward so that the dragonfly could grip the front of its nymphal skin. But when I released my finger, the dragonfly fell back. About five minutes later, with a mighty effort, the dragonfly looped up, stretched out its legs, and gripped the head of its old skin. It then pulled out the tip of its abdomen and hung free.

The dragonfly was pale brown, its small wings were moist and crumpled, and its huge eyes met on the top of its head. After a short rest it crawled forward onto the stick. Now its wings started to expand. They hung together above the dragonfly's back. They did not grow, but blood was being pumped into the network of wing veins, forcing them apart till they looked like pale green gauze. So the wings were stretched wider and increased in length. Their tips moved out and downward at twice the speed of the minute hand of my watch. In twenty minutes the wings had reached full size. They

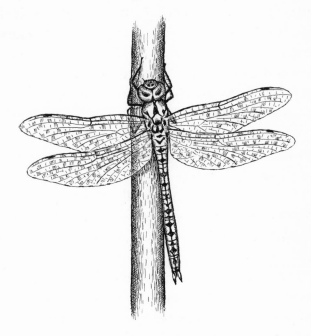

dragonfly, showing position of wings at rest

soon became transparent and glittered with pearly lights. Meanwhile the abdomen had grown longer and more slender. Some drops of clear liquid were squeezed out from its tip and fell into the aquarium.

Half an hour later the dragonfly's body began to take on color. Its thorax and abdomen showed tints of yellow, green, and blue between darker lines and spots. Gradually its legs grew dark and its eyes became a luminous green. An hour later the yellows, blues and greens of its body had become bright and vivid. Then once, twice, three times, the dragonfly flicked its wings about an inch apart. Suddenly it opened them wide, then spread them stiffly sideways in their true position of rest. Five minutes later the wings began to flutter and vibrate. I put my finger under the dragonfly's body and pressed gently upward. The dragonfly let go of the stick and clutched my finger with its legs.

Now, with the dragonfly on my finger, I went out into the garden. As the sunshine warmed its brilliant body, the dragonfly fluttered its wings faster and faster. Then, with a dry rustling sound, it rose into the air, circled above the garden, and flew swiftly away between the trees.

Dragonflies are swift and powerful fliers. They fly with their bristly legs held forward to trap mosquitoes, midges, mayflies, and other insects, which they capture in midair. The long-bodied hawker dragonflies eat their prey on the wing. However, the smaller and rather stouter darter dragonflies, which hatch from the broad, squat nymphs, usually wait on the tips of prominent twigs or stems. From these lookout posts they dart out to capture flying insects, then return to their perches to feed.

The hawker dragonflies often have regular beats of thirty yards, or so, in extent. Along these beats they hunt their prey and drive away any rival dragonfly that happens to intrude. Once, when I was watching a hawker dragonfly flying up and down its stretch of country lane, a cabbage butterfly flew past me. It did not fly far, for the dragonfly darted forward and captured it. A few seconds later the butterfly's wings drifted down, one after the other, like the falling petals of a white flower, from the jaws of the flying dragonfly.

After about three weeks of hunting insects over hedgerows and along the edge of woods, dragonflies make their way to ponds, slow rivers, or lakes. Above the water the male dragonfly pursues a female, clutches her behind the head with the claspers at the tip of his abdomen, and the pair settles among the reeds to mate. After mating, the female hawker dragonflies lay their eggs in stems or leaves of water plants, while the darters drop theirs in the water as they fly over its surface.

Included in the dragonfly order of insects are the damselflies. These are smaller and altogether more delicate creatures. Their flight is rather slow and fluttering; and they rest with wings closed above their backs, not outspread like those of dragonflies.

Damselfly nymphs are slender insects with wide

heads, large eyes, longish legs, and tapering abdomens, each nicely finished at the tip by three fine, leaf-like gills. Though their coloring is fairly drab, being greenish, or yellowish-brown, the nymphs of damselflies have a certain elegance, which those of dragonflies entirely lack.

Damselfly nymphs swim with a sideways wriggling motion of the abdomen, aided by the leaf-like gills, which act as tail fins. They swim more readily than dragonfly nymphs, but spend most of their time clinging to the stems of water plants. When resting on the plants in my aquarium, they often wave their tail ends to and fro very gracefully. They do this to keep a flow of water over their gills.

damselfly nymph

So far there seems little to suggest that damselflies and dragonflies are closely related. Their nymphs do not look much alike, and they breathe and swim in very different ways. However, they are identical in their method of catching prey. In damselfly nymphs the lower lip is a mask which works in exactly the same way as that of the nymphs of dragonflies. This kind of food-catching apparatus has never been developed from the lower lip of any other insect. It shows, more than any other feature,

the kinship that links the damselflies to the dragonflies.

Most of the damselflies from
my aquarium emerge in May or
June. The nymphs climb out of
the water and up the stick provided, usually between eight and
eleven o'clock in the morning.
They normally come to rest
facing upward, though two of
the nymphs that I watched, for
some reason known only to themselves, turned around after climbing the stick and faced downward. These two damselflies, after
extricating themselves from the
nymphal skins, had to reverse their position. Had
they not done so, their moist wings would have
flopped downward while expanding and would then
have hardened in a bent and crumpled state.

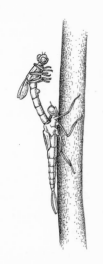

*damselfly emerging
from the
nymphal case*

The body of an emerging damselfly does not
arch over and hang downward like that of a dragonfly. It remains straight and projects forward from
the front of the nymph's thorax. Thus, a damselfly
does not have to make the effort to loop its body
upward. After a short rest, it merely bends forward,
grasps the stick in front of the nymphal skin, then
lifts out the tip of its abdomen.

When freshly emerged, the damselflies from my

aquarium are very pale and fragile-looking creatures. They are almost white, tinted with yellow or pinkish-brown. Their legs are colorless and almost transparent, their abdomens short, and their wings like tiny brownish bags. After resting for about a quarter of an hour, they start expanding their wings. Some rock their abdomens up and down about twice a second when their wings begin to lengthen. They probably do this to aid the pumping of blood into their wing veins. As the wings expand, they turn a cloudy yellow-green color. They expand quickly, reaching their full length in about ten minutes, and then become clear and transparent.

damselfly, showing position of wings at rest

Some fifteen minutes later the abdomen starts to lengthen. At first it is about two thirds the length of the expanded wings. It extends rapidly, and usually takes only ten minutes to more than double its length and reach full size. As it lengthens, the abdomen becomes more and more slender until it is half the thickness of a match stick, but slightly swollen at the tip.

About half an hour after their abdomens have lengthened, my damselflies become fully colored—most of them grayish blue with darker lines; but some, of another kind, bright red. As soon as they are ready to fly I take them out into the garden. Here they flutter above the lawn, their delicate wings twinkling in the sunlight until they settle on a leaf or stem. After a short rest in the sunshine, they hover gently upward, then drift away on sparkling wings and vanish in the distance.

damselfly in flight

8. Mayflies

Mayfly nymphs are very common in the ponds I visit. They struggle violently in the net; and, when released from it into the pie dish, they dart about at great speed.

There are many kinds of mayfly nymphs. Some kinds climb about on the water plants; some crawl over the muddy beds of rivers; some actually burrow in the muddy banks of ponds; some cling closely to stones and boulders in swift mountain streams; and some, like the ones I find, are good swimmers, preferring still water.

My mayfly nymphs are delicate, torpedo-shaped creatures, about a third of an inch long when fully grown. They are widest behind the head, and taper almost to a point at the hind end. This supports three feathery tail pieces, marked with a dark band near their tips. The nymphs are light greenish-gray in color, somewhat transparent and slightly mottled; but when fully grown they become darkish brown. The legs are slender and the antennae so fine and transparent that, except at the base, they can hardly be seen, even under a pocket lens. The thorax, in all but very young nymphs, bears two wing buds; and the abdomen has seven pairs of leaf-like gills along its sides. The first six pairs of gills are double, like two tiny leaves joined at their base, but the last pair is single.

The gills are in an upright position, so that when I view a mayfly nymph from above with a pocket lens, they appear as thin lines sticking out from each side of its body. But from the front I can see their roundish-oval shape. With the aid of the lens I can also watch the fascinating motion of the nymph's gills: they flicker back and forth, suddenly, at irregular intervals, once or several times a minute. The gills on each side of the nymph's abdomen beat together in perfect unison.

The movement of a mayfly nymph's gills is so rapid that it is extremely difficult to follow. However, careful watching has shown me that, except for the last pair, which remain still, the gills close against the nymph's body in succession from the front backward; then open from the back forward. Thus, when the gills flickered, I could see a pulse of motion run down and up each side of the nymph's abdomen. This caused a current, bringing fresh supplies of water to the gills.

My mayfly nymphs feed on the microscopic green plants that cover the stones and smear the glass of the aquarium. I have watched them nibbling away at the stone surfaces with their tiny jaws, every now

*mayfly nymphs eating the green film of
minute plants on a stone*

and then stepping forward to nibble a new patch,
like sheep grazing on a hillside. Suddenly, one of the
nymphs will cease feeding and swim to another
stone, a water plant, or the side of the aquarium.

The swimming motion of the mayfly nymphs is
beautiful to see. They dart through the water at high
speed by means of rapid up and down flicks of the
abdomen, aided by their feathery tail pieces. They
start at full speed from a standing position, and
finish just as suddenly, sometimes in mid-water; then
they sink slowly downward, often shooting forward
again before they reach the bottom.

At the end of May, and during June, July, and
August, the adult mayflies start emerging from my
aquarium. In order to watch this process as closely as
possible, I placed a number of nymphs in the small

plastic box aquarium. I soon discovered that, when a full-grown mayfly nymph was nearly ready to cast its skin, its gills would start to flicker continuously, instead of in short spasms. At the same time the nymph became restless and darted through the water at frequent intervals. I found this a very useful discovery. As soon as I saw a nymph vibrating its gills steadily, I kept it under observation. Soon I would notice a silvery sheen beneath the nymph's skin. This was due to a film of air collecting under the skin. The gills of water creatures absorb air which has dissolved in the water. Thus, the continuous, rapid beating of the mayfly nymph's gills, at this stage, probably helps to form the film of extra air beneath its skin.

Before this stage, the mayfly nymph had been heavier than water, but now, with the air beneath its skin, the nymph became buoyant. It floated to the surface whenever it stopped swimming or released its hold on the side of the plastic box. Soon the nymph was resting motionless at the surface of the water. Suddenly it twisted its abdomen up and down as though straining, then pressed back its legs. The next moment its skin split, and the mayfly stepped out onto the water and flew off, landing on the window pane. The mayfly emerged with its wings fully expanded, and the whole process, from the splitting of the nymph's skin to the flight of the mayfly from the water, took only about two seconds.

On examining the nymphal skin as it floated on the water, I saw that it had split along the top of the head and thorax, which had opened sideways to form a more or less circular raft. This held the rest of the skin steady and enabled the mayfly to emerge without tilting over before its legs came free to support it on the water-film. Now I understood why the film of air had formed under the nymph's skin. It caused the nymph to float so that the mayfly could emerge on top of the water. Also it left a dry inner surface to the nymphal skin. This prevented the skin from sinking as the mayfly pulled itself out.

mayfly sub-imago just emerged
from the floating nymphal case

I examined the mayfly as soon as it had settled on the window pane. Its slender body was dull brown, and its abdomen curved upward toward the tip, from which two fine tail-threads extended. Its fragile wings were pale smoky gray, and they stood upright and closed together above its thorax. Its middle and hind legs were short, but the front pair was much longer and extended forward beyond its head. The antennae were very short, like tiny bristles, and the two prominent, upward-facing eyes, which stood on top of the mayfly's head, showed me that it was a male. The female mayfly's eyes, which I describe later, are quite different.

As I watched the mayfly, its two tail threads started to lengthen. In a few minutes they had doubled their original length and were fully extended. They were now a little longer than the rest of the mayfly's body and pointed back and outward from the tip of its abdomen. The mayfly had not yet completed its development, however. It would not grow any more, but several hours later it would moult again and emerge with clear, transparent wings, long tail threads, and slightly longer front legs.

The nymphs and larvae of all insects undergo a number of moults as they grow, becoming a little bigger after each moult. However, mayflies are the only insects which actually moult after having wings and being able to fly.

After emerging from the nymphal skin, and before its final moult, the mayfly is known as the sub-imago. The sub-imago never flies far. After emerging from the pond it flies to a nearby bush, tree trunk, or clump of reeds, where it settles and waits for the final moult. I found that the sub-imago mayflies which emerged from my aquarium in the morning moulted in the afternoon of the same day. Those that emerged in the afternoon or evening, however, did not moult until the next morning. After moulting the mayfly is now fully adult.

I have spent many hours waiting for sub-imago mayflies to moult, as they rested in glass jars or on the window pane. Often I had to interrupt my watching for some errand or for a meal, only to find, on my return, that an adult mayfly had emerged in my absence.

At last, however, I was on the spot at the right moment. I watched a sub-imago move a few steps up the glass, then tap the surface with its legs as if to get a firmer grip. Its wings, which had been held together above its thorax, then opened slightly apart, and its abdomen jerked up and down. Suddenly it became very agitated. Its abdomen trembled and its wings opened wider, spread sideways, then stretched backward as its head and thorax split. At once the head and thorax of the adult mayfly pushed up and out, and its body came smoothly forward. As its wings were drawn out I could see the wings of the sub-imago gradually shrink and shrivel to tiny lumps of skin. Once free, the adult's wings opened sideways and its body tipped backward. For a second the mayfly hung by the tip of its abdomen, then it looped up and clutched the glass surface above the head of the cast skin. It then raised its abdomen up between its wings to release the long tail-threads, and stepped sideways away from the empty skin. The whole process, from the moment the sub-imago spread its wings, took about seven seconds.

One sub-imago, after emerging from the water, rested upside down on the wire netting that covers my aquarium. From this position the adult mayfly, on emerging, was unable to heave itself up and clutch the wire. It fell into the water, where it floated with outspread wings. Quickly I got a soft paintbrush and lifted it out, but its frail wings crumpled up and stuck to the brush. I flicked the mayfly onto a piece of card and left it on the windowsill to dry out. For a few moments its legs quivered feebly, then it lay still, as if dead, fixed by its damp wings to the card. After drying out, the mayfly started to revive, but its wings were still bent and crumpled, and despite its struggles it was unable to stand upright. There was nothing I could do. It seemed strange that, after living for a year in the water as a nymph, the mayfly was hopelessly crippled when its wings had touched the surface.

Adult mayflies are among the most delicate and dainty of all insects. Their mouth parts are minute and useless, for during their brief lives they never feed. Their stomachs are filled with air, and act as balloons to buoy them up, so that they can use their little store of energy as effectively as possible in flying. This energy is used in the dancing flight of males, while females use it, after mating, in their egg-laying flight above the water.

Most kinds of mayfly have two pairs of wings, the hind pair being very short; but the mayflies from my aquarium have only one pair, the hind wings being absent. These mayflies also differ from most others in having two tail-threads instead of three.

Male and female mayflies emerge from my aquarium in roughly equal numbers. They are easy to tell apart. The males are dark brown with slender abdomens, tail-threads nearly twice the length of their bodies, long front legs, and wings so transparent as to be hardly visible. The females, on the other hand, are pale brownish or greenish yellow, their abdomens are less slender, their tail-threads and front legs slightly shorter, and their wings clearly visible, being yellowish brown along the front border.

The most remarkable difference between these male and female mayflies, however, is in the formation of their eyes. In the males, the upper and lower halves of both eyes have separated and moved apart to make four distinct eyes. The upper eyes are large and bright red brown. They face upward and are raised above the head, so that, seen from the side, the mayfly looks as if it were wearing a peculiar kind of hat. The lower eyes are smaller, black, and face

sideways. In the females,
the eyes are yellowish-
brown. They face side-
ways and are not sepa-
rated into distinct halves,
but marked with a double
line across the middle.
The upper eyes of the
male mayflies must be
specially useful for spot-
ting a female as she flies
above them during their
dancing flight.

Sometimes, on a warm,
sunny morning, several
mayflies emerge from
my aquarium. Then, in
the afternoon, when they
have cast their final skins
and become true adults,
I take them out in an
open box and place it on
the garden table. All
through the afternoon
and early evening the
mayflies rest with wings
closed above their backs.
Then, at about half an
hour before sunset, they

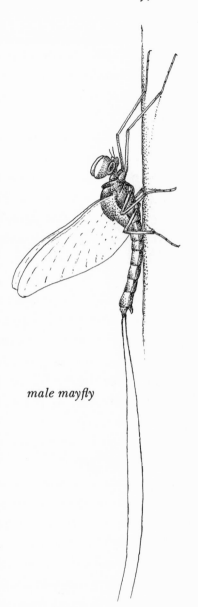

male mayfly

begin to stir, open and close their wings, and crawl up the sides of the box. A few minutes later, one after the other, they fly up into the evening air.

female mayfly

The female mayflies fly up at a steep angle and flutter away out of sight; but the males fly only to the edge of the syca- more tree that stands beside my hedge. The branches of the tree, showing up against the evening sky, act as markers for their eyes, and hold the may- flies in position as they perform the mating dance. Having flown upward to a height of about twelve or fifteen feet from the ground, they begin to drift down, and then fly vertically up again. Up and down they fly, in a steady, rhythmic dance. Soon, other mayflies from the neighborhood join them, until a loose swarm of about a dozen males has formed.

I stand, transfixed, my eyes following the up-and-down rhythm of the dancing mayflies. The rays of the setting sun sparkle like fire on their delicate wings as they beat the air on the upward flight. They fly from four to six feet upward and then drift down for the same distance. Sometimes two or three may- flies fly up and down in unison, but at slightly different heights. The descent, with their bodies horizontal, is slower than the upward flight, and at the base of each descent they make a sudden upward curve, tilting their bodies for the swifter climb. This fast-slow rhythm of the dancing males is fascinating and beautiful to watch.

At first I am uncertain whether the mayflies are fluttering or parachuting downward. The action of their transparent wings is very difficult to follow. However, by standing directly beneath a mayfly, I can just make out its wings, outspread and still, as it descends. Then the wings suddenly disappear in a whirl of flight as the mayfly swings up and retraces its vertical path through the air above me.

Often a mayfly, on reaching the top of its upward flight, pursues a passing gnat or fly for a short way, and then falls back to continue its dance. Occasionally I spot a female mayfly approaching the swarm in a gentle, steady flight. As she reaches it, she is immediately clutched from below by the long, upheld front legs of a male. The coupled pair fly out of the swarm and quickly disappear into the distance.

Soon after the sun has set, but before the warm glow has faded from the west, the mayflies disperse and settle to sleep on stems and leaves. Some, perhaps, will dance the following evening, while others —their energies exhausted—die in their sleep. The coupled pairs, after a brief mating, part, and the males flutter feebly downward—their last stores of energy used up in this final act.

The female mayflies, however, after mating are still full of life. They fly off to the nearest stretch of water—in this case, probably, some garden pond. There, each female performs a dipping flight above the surface, shooting eggs into the water at the base of each aerial curve. Then, as the last eggs leave her body and sink downward, the mayfly falls exhausted on the water surface.

I often see the pale bodies and outspread wings of floating female mayflies as I walk beside ponds on summer evenings. Having spent themselves in securing a new generation of mayflies, the females give themselves up to the water that was once their home. Sooner or later a fish, a backswimmer, or a pond skater finds them, and their dead bodies nourish the continuing life of the pond.

exhausted female mayfly floating on the water

9. The Water Bugs

So far, I have told you about insects that spend their young growing stages in the water, but as adults leave it and become airborne. Now I turn to the insects that spend their whole lives under water, except for brief periods when, as adults, some fly from one pond to another. This mostly happens if a pond gets overcrowded, if it does not contain enough food, or if, during a drought, it starts drying up. However, these insects do frequently leave what seems to be a perfectly suitable pond and travel to another. Perhaps they do this simply because they like, or perhaps need, to exercise their powers of flight.

Among the most common insects that live under water as adults are some of the water bugs. Bugs, in general, form a large and important insect order. One of their chief characteristics is an absence of biting jaws: their mouth parts take the form of a beak-like, sucking tube, often used for piercing plants or animal prey. Also, their young are nymphs. Most bugs live on land, but a few, such as the back-swimmer, the lesser water boatman, and the water scorpion, have become adapted to underwater life. The pond skater is a bug that lives on the water surface.

The lesser water boatmen are the most abundant and widespread of all the water bugs. Look into a clear patch of almost any pond, and you are likely to see them swimming rapidly here and there over the muddy bottom. When you catch them in the net, they leap and skip about on their fronts or backs by kicking vigorously backward with their hind legs. While on their backs, the lesser water boatmen look

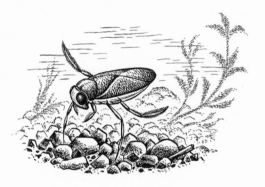

lesser water boatman

very conspicuous, for the underside of their bodies is yellowish-white. The upper surface is dark brownish-gray except for the rounded head which, apart from the large, dark eyes, is also yellowish-white. The thorax is marked with very fine black lines, and the fore wings are densely stippled with minute black dots. The fore wings are firm and scale-like, and act as protective covers to the filmy, transparent hind wings.

When a lesser water boatman is swimming in the aquarium, its underside appears to be glistening silver. This is because the underside is covered with an air bubble that the water boatman uses for breathing. The lesser water boatman swims fast but in a very jerky fashion. It swims with its long, oar-like hind legs, the end parts of which are feathered with stiff hairs along their inner edge. The hairs help to give extra push against the water when the legs thrust backward. The middle legs are long and slender and each has a pair of fine, sharp claws at its tip. These legs are used for holding on to stones or plant stems when the water boatman rests. (It has to hold on to objects under water while it rests; otherwise, being lighter than water, it would bob up to the surface like a cork.) The front legs are very short and are used for sifting the bottom ooze and debris when the water boatman is feeding. These legs also serve another purpose which I shall come to later.

When lesser water boatmen are very young nymphs, and before they develop wing buds, they are able to breathe air dissolved in the water through their delicate skins. After this early stage, however, they breathe free air and must surface at frequent intervals to renew their supply. This air is held as a bubble on the underside of the thorax and around the abdomen by patches of minute, unwettable hairs.

When it is ready to renew its air supply, the lesser water boatman darts to the top of the water. Its back breaks the surface-film, and it immediately swims down again. In the instant when its back is above the surface, fresh air enters the crevice between the water boatman's head and thorax and replenishes the bubble. The air is breathed into the body of the water boatman through minute holes, the spiracles, placed along its sides.

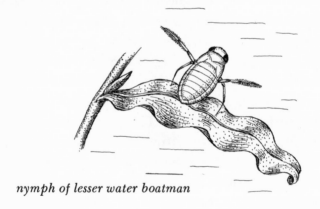

nymph of lesser water boatman

The nymphs of lesser water boatmen are active swimmers and look very like the adults. When newly hatched they are pale yellow-brown in color. Wing buds appear after the first moult, and the nymphs then become darker brown. As with all insects, they grow in a series of stages following each moult. When the lesser boatman nymph is about to change its skin, it enters a tangle of waterweeds and clutches a stem. After it has cast its old skin, the nymph is entirely yellowish-white except for its dark eyes. It clings to the plant stem until its new skin hardens and it regains its normal color.

The lesser water boatman is a useful scavenger, and I have often watched one feeding at the bottom of my aquarium. It holds on to the gravel with its middle legs, then bends forward and tosses up little puffs of silt and debris by swinging its short front legs rapidly up and down. As it does this, the short sucking tube under its head draws in microscopic plants and particles of decayed plant and animal matter below the silt.

At rest on a stone, a plant stem, or the gravel, the lesser water boatman holds its hind legs extended up and sideways, and flips them backward and forward at frequent intervals. This action, which causes a current to pass over the insect's body, helps waste air, breathed out into the surrounding bubble, to dissolve away in the water. At the same time it allows fresh air, dissolved in the water, to diffuse into the bubble. However, the water boatman cannot replenish the air in its bubble completely in this way, and sooner or later must dart to the surface for a proper supply.

Another use the lesser water boatman makes of its hind legs is to keep the upper surface of its body clean. I have often watched one repeatedly bend its hind legs forward and sweep them back from its head over its thorax and wing covers—using the stiff hairs on these legs to brush away any particles of dirt.

One evening when I happened to be sitting near my aquarium, I heard a faint but shrill noise that sounded like *cre-e-e, cre-e-e, cre-e-e*. The noise was repeated every few minutes. At first I thought it must be a house cricket chirping, but then I realized that the sound was coming from my aquarium. Perhaps one of the creatures was scratching at the glass side in an attempt to get out. I went to see what was going on. As I watched, a water boatman alighted on one of the big stones. Then the sound came clear and shrill, *cre-e-e, cre-e-e, cre-e-e*. It seemed to issue from the water boatman, but I was still not sure. The water boatman left the stone, swam forward, and alighted on the gravel just by the glass front of the aquarium. The noise was repeated. This time there was no doubt about it—the chirping sound was made by the water boatman.

I was tremendously excited by this discovery, for I had no idea that lesser water boatmen could actually chirp, like grasshoppers and crickets. However, on consulting my natural history books, I read that the males do at times make a chirping noise, which is thought to be a mating call.

Before alighting on a stone to chirp, the lesser water boatman swims in a rather pretty fashion. It hovers, or flutters, so to speak, above the stone with very short but rapid flips of its hind legs. When actually chirping (or stridulating, to use the correct word), the water boatman vibrates its front legs against the lower portion of its head, making a blur of movement. The legs have minute teeth on their inner surface which scrape a ridge on each side of the water boatman's head, so causing the noise. There seems to be a sort of sounding board in the head to amplify this noise, for when a water boatman bumps against the side of the aquarium, the sound its head makes on the glass is surprisingly loud.

Lesser water boatmen sometimes take flight on warm, sunny days during the summer. I have seen them fly down and alight on the water, then push apart the surface-film with their hind legs and dive below. I have also seen a water boatman in my aquarium dart full speed to the top of the water, break through the surface into the air, and take flight before it could fall back. Its flight was short, however, for it bumped against the window and fell down on the sill. I rescued it and dropped it back in the aquarium.

Lesser water boatmen are active and usually plentiful in ponds, so they are easily seen and captured; but there is another water bug which, though common, is much more difficult to find. This is the water scorpion.

The water scorpion likes to stay in the shallow water near the edge of the pond, where there are plenty of water plants. Here it rests among the plants or on the muddy bottom just below them.

When you scoop up a water scorpion in the net it remains perfectly still, its dark brown color and flat shape making it look like a dead and water-logged leaf. Thus you have to search very carefully for it, and must examine everything in your net that looks like an old, brown leaf about an inch in length. You are, in fact, quite likely to pick up a water scorpion before you realize it; for the creature will not give itself away by moving, even when held and turned between your fingers. However, when placed in the water of the pie dish, the water scorpion soon recovers from the shock of being caught. It cautiously stretches out its legs, then starts to swim or crawl over the bottom of the dish.

The water scorpion swims in a slow, jerky fashion by kicking backward with its middle and hind pairs of legs. You will notice that the legs are rather slender and not adapted in any particular way for swimming. This is because the water scorpion does not swim much, but relies on stillness and on its leaf-like appearance, to avoid its enemies and to catch its prey. In fact, it only swims when it wants to move from one group of water plants to another, or from the surface to the bottom of the ponds. Its middle and hind legs are used chiefly for crawling, clamber-

ing among water plants, or clinging to them as it
lurks in wait for prey.

You might think that the water scorpion has
only four legs, for its front ones are specialized for
catching prey, and look like pincers. These legs are
fairly thick, and project forward on each side of the
creature's head. From there they spread out sideways then bend abruptly inward. The inward-
turned portion of each front leg ends in a sharp claw,
and is hinged so that it moves sideways. It can be
folded into a groove on the outspread part of the leg
in the same way as the blade of a penknife folds into
the handle.

A mayfly nymph or some creature of similar size
which comes within range of the water scorpion has
little chance. Quick as a flash the scorpion lurches
forward, flicks open the nearest front leg, then closes
it on the prey with a vise-like grip. If some larger
creature, such as a full-grown damselfly nymph,
should come its way, the water scorpion flicks out
both pincer-legs together and holds it securely in a
double grip.

Between the bases of its front legs, you can see the
water scorpion's head. It seems ridiculously tiny
for the size of its body. The small eyes are prominent
and bulge sideways, and the sucking tube, correctly
called the rostrum, is short and sharp. The rostrum
is not bent underneath the head as in most bugs, but
projects forward between the water scorpion's eyes

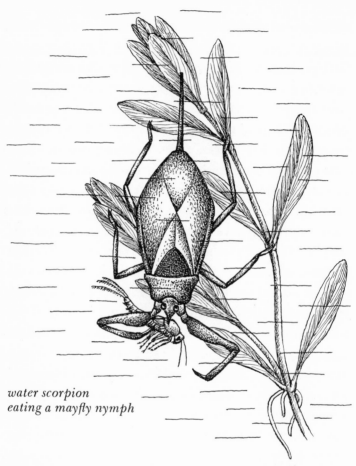

*water scorpion
eating a mayfly nymph*

like an acutely pointed nose. After seizing its prey,
the water scorpion pierces the victim with the sharp
tip of its rostrum and injects it with a paralyzing
saliva to stop it moving. It then slowly and peacefully sucks the body juices of the limp creature, until
only an empty skin is left to float away.

You will notice that the water scorpion has a

slender, bristle-like tail projecting backward from the hind end of its body. This tail, which is about half an inch long, looks suspiciously like a stinging instrument, but is, in fact, quite harmless. Nonetheless, the water scorpion was so named on account of its tail and pincer-like front legs. These two features reminded people of the stinging tail and pincers of the real scorpions that live in warm countries. However, true scorpions have nothing in common with the water bugs. They are not even insects, but have eight legs and belong to the class of creatures which includes the spiders, harvestmen and mites. What then, is the purpose of the water scorpion's tail?

It is a kind of snorkel or breathing tube, formed from two hair-like tailpieces, grooved along their inner edge, and held together to form a hollow bristle. Through this hollow bristle, which pierces the water-film, the water scorpion is able to breathe free air while it rests, head downward on a plant stem, just below the surface. Two spiracles at the base of this breathing tube allow air to enter the water scorpion's body. When the water scorpion descends further below the surface, the air is still held in its breathing tube, so it is able to remain down for some time. When it does require a fresh supply of air, the water scorpion climbs slowly backward up the plant stem until the tip of the tube again breaks the surface-film.

When its breathing tube is freshly filled with air,

the water scorpion floats, but when the air starts to get used up it becomes heavier than water. It is then unable, with its thin legs, to swim up to the surface. Thus, if it is on the bottom of a pond and away from the edge, it must rely on nearby plant stems, up which it can climb to reach the air. For this reason it is very important that the water scorpion should not stray into deep water where the tops of the water plants are below the surface. To prevent this from happening, there are special sense organs on the water scorpion's body which enable it to know at all times how far down it happens to be.

In the nymphs of water scorpions, which are broader and more squat in shape than the adults, the breathing tube is very short. In young nymphs it is no more than a slight projection at the hind end of the abdomen. The nymphs of water scorpions spend nearly all their time at the tops of water plants with their short breathing tubes at the surface. They rarely climb down the plant stems. The adults occasionally swim down to the bottom of the aquarium, but I have never seen a nymph attempt to do so.

water scorpion nymph

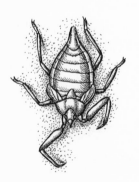

The three water scorpions at present in my aquarium were half-grown nymphs when I col-

lected them in June, and they all became adult in
August. They make very little movement and, except
when grasping prey, their actions are rather slow.
They remain perfectly still, clinging head downward
to plant stems for long periods, and when they do
move it is usually to obtain a fresh supply of air.
However, I find nothing dull about the stillness of a
water scorpion. I have often gazed at one for ten or
fifteen minutes, and though it made hardly any
movement, it held my interest throughout the time.
This is because the stillness of a water scorpion is its
way of life. It is the stillness of a poised and expect-
ant predator awaiting the moment when its prey approaches. It might even be said that keeping still is
the water scorpion's particular way of being active.
Try keeping perfectly still, as I have often done
while watching some wild creature, and you will
soon find the muscles in various parts of your body
beginning to ache and tire.

When I remove a water scorpion from my aquarium and place it on the table, it takes on another
kind of stillness. This time it is very like the stillness
of death, and the water scorpion is no longer interesting to watch. I simply wait and wait, for five, ten,
forty minutes or more
for it to make a move-
ment. In this death-
like pose the water
scorpion holds its

water scorpion shamming

pincer-legs, usually folded, above its head, while the other two pairs are held stiffly backward below its abdomen. Even when placed on its back, the water scorpion maintains this pose and makes no attempt to right itself.

Sooner or later, however, the water scorpion recovers from the shock of being removed from the aquarium. Its pincer-legs gradually fall sideways. Some minutes later its middle and hind legs quiver, then open outward, and it starts walking quite rapidly over the table. While walking, it turns its pincer-legs tip downward and moves them alternately in keeping with its other legs, much as a man would help himself along with two walking sticks. When the water scorpion reaches the end of the table, it crawls down to the edge of the tablecloth, then drops on to the floor. Should it land on its back, it quickly levers itself over by pressing down and backwards with one extended pincer-leg. It then continues its hurried progress until I pick it up. In my fingers it again adopts the death-like pose, but when I drop it into the aquarium it soon recovers and swims to the nearest water plant.

Although the adult water scorpion has a pair of flying wings beneath its brown wing covers, I have never been able to persuade my own specimens to fly. In the hope that, perhaps, one of my water scorpions might attempt to take wing, I kept them out of water for a time, and allowed them to walk freely on various raised surfaces. However, on reaching the edge of any surface, they simply toppled over it and fell, with tightly closed wings, on to the floor.

However, there is another, much rarer kind of water scorpion, often called the stick scorpion, which certainly does fly. I happen to know this, because, one sunny morning when I was away on holiday, and walking beside a slow stream, a stick scorpion flew on to my jacket. It paused on my jacket for a moment, then opened its wings, revealing, to my surprise, a flame-red abdomen, and flew away. I shall always remember how the mud-brown stick scorpion was suddenly transformed into a creature of dazzling color as it took off and sailed away in the sunshine.

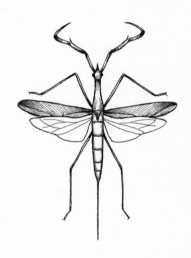

stick scorpion with wings outspread

The stick scorpion is a larger insect than the water scorpion, and long and slender. When you lift it from the net, it will resemble a piece of stick instead of a dead leaf.

10. Water Beetles

The commonest and best known of water beetles are the carnivorous water beetles. These are lively and interesting beetles to watch, and they do very well in an aquarium. All they need for food, apart from the creatures they capture, is an occasional dead worm or a morsel of meat.

Carnivorous water beetles are excellently fitted for life in their watery world. Their shining, oval bodies slip smoothly through the water, as the long, flattened hind legs, fringed with close-set, stiff hairs, row them speedily here and there over the pond bed.

All water beetles, like those that live on land, breathe free air from above the surface. Having no gills they cannot breathe air dissolved in the water. They carry a supply with them, but must surface from time to time in order to renew it. A carnivorous water beetle which wishes to renew its air supply starts to swim upward; then, as it approaches the surface, stops swimming, and being lighter than water, rises, hind-end uppermost, till the tip of its abdomen breaks the surface-film. Sometimes, when an impatient water beetle, after

a long spell below, is rising rather slowly to the
surface, it helps itself upward by reversing the
swimming motion of its
hind legs, as one would
reverse the strokes of the
oars when backing a
rowing boat from a river
bank. I have occasionally
seen this in my aquarium.

As the carnivorous
water beetle breaks the
surface-film, it raises its

*carnivorous water beetle
taking in air at the surface*

wing covers slightly, causing a fresh supply of air to
rush in below them. The water beetle usually pauses
for a few seconds, suspended from the surface-film
by the tip of its abdomen, before swimming down
again. It shows none of the desperate hurry of the
more delicate water boatmen to return below, for
its body is protected by a hard, horny covering.

When the water beetle lowers its wing covers and
swims down, the trapped air-bubble is held between
the underside of the wing covers and the top of its
abdomen, which is slightly hollowed. In most insects the breathing holes, or spiracles, are placed
along the sides of the abdomen, but the spiracles of
a carnivorous water beetle are on the top, so that
air from the bubble can enter them.

The wing covers of the carnivorous water beetle fit tightly against the edges of its abdomen to hold the air-bubble firmly against its back and to prevent any water from seeping in while the beetle remains below the surface. The hard wing covers of all beetles are really their front pair of wings, which have lost the power of flight movement and have become stiff and horny, to serve as a protective covering. The transparent flying wings are folded beneath them, when not in use.

Some ground-living beetles have become flightless and rely on their ability to run fast or hide beneath logs and stones to escape their enemies; then the wing covers are sometimes firmly fused together along their inner edge. The wing covers of these beetles, which cannot be pushed apart, form a solid protective shield against being crushed or easily bitten.

However, all water beetles are able to fly, and their open wing covers act as stabilizers as they travel through the air, propelled by their long, transparent flight wings.

The ability to fly enables water beetles to disperse to other ponds in the neighborhood when their own becomes overcrowded, or lacks sufficient food. This is particularly important for many carnivorous water beetles which like to inhabit small, shallow pools of water that are little more than outsize puddles; these quickly dry up in times of summer drought.

I have discovered, however, that not all the carnivorous water beetles leave a pond or ditch when it dries up. While exploring the dried beds of ponds in summer, I have sometimes found them resting beneath stones, sodden logs, or piles of stranded water plants. I have even dug them up with a trowel from cracks and crevices in the drying mud. The beetles were quietly waiting for the next rainfall to refill their home. After all, being air breathers, water beetles can wait quite comfortably for the rain to come, and while they remain inactive, they can survive for a long time without food.

Really, we know very little about the forces that act on an insect's senses, and guide it in its various movements. Water beetles might possibly be encouraged to fly by changes of a few degrees in the temperature of their pond, by the amount of moisture in the air above it, by the direction of the wind, by the cloudiness or clearness of the sky, or by a particular phase of the moon. They might leave a pond because there are not enough microscopic plants to give the water taste, or because they dislike the faint trace of some particular chemical dissolving in the water from the bed or the surrounding soil. Other conditions, such as being ready to mate, might cause them to take wing. There is an enormous amount to be discovered.

Carnivorous water beetles usually fly at night. In summer I have occasionally watched one come buzzing through the window, circle the light, bump against the ceiling a few times, then drop to the floor and lie kicking and spinning on its back. To save such misguided water beetles I have dropped them into my aquarium.

Water beetles have quite large eyes, and as they wing their way over the dark landscape, they recognize a pond below them by the light of the sky or moon reflecting from the surface of the water.

They also sometimes fly by day. I once hit one with my hand as it was flying over a meadow in bright sunlight. It was a shining black water beetle, about half an inch in length. It flipped about in my hand for a few minutes after being picked up, then clambered awkwardly along my finger, spread its wings, took off, and continued its journey. Water beetles from my aquarium have also taken flight on warm sunny days. In such weather they like to climb out of the water and air themselves on the leaves of frogbit, or up the stick that I keep for emerging dragonflies. It is from these places that they sometimes fly.

Although carnivorous water beetles are able to locate fresh ponds by sight when they are flying, they seem to find their food underwater chiefly by smell and touch. They have fairly long, thread-like antennae, and these are what they smell with. I have described in the introductory chapter how my water beetles swim in circles above a dead worm, and gradually discover its position by scent. In a similar way they frequently swim in twists and circles here and there over the bottom of the aquarium, as if trying to trace the scent of some creature to its source. Dead creatures, as they start to decay, give off a stronger scent than living creatures, and they are much more quickly found by water beetles.

When carnivorous water beetles do capture living prey, it seems to be almost the result of an accident. For instance, if a tadpole or damselfly nymph happens to bump into a swimming water beetle, the beetle clutches it and starts at once to chew the creature with its hard, biting jaws. However, if such a prey should escape before it is firmly clutched, the water beetle makes no attempt to pursue it by sight, but swims about in a rather bewildered manner, as if trying to trace its scent. Carnivorous water beetles, in fact, seem to rely so much on their sense of smell in finding prey under water, that they forget to use their eyes. Yet the slightest movement that I make above a water beetle taking in air at the surface of a pond sends it diving full speed to the bottom.

The largest carnivorous water beetles suitable for the aquarium are about half an inch in length. Of the kinds of these that I find most frequently, one is shining black and the other dull brown with yellowish edges. The black water beetles are smooth and rapid swimmers, and look very spectacular as they speed here and there over the bottom of the aquarium, float up for air, pause for a few seconds, then race down again. The yellow-bordered brown ones are a little slower and more jerky in their movements.

Next in size come two water beetles about a fifth of an inch long, both of which are common in the ponds and ditches near my home. Most carnivorous water beetles are very similar in shape, and take the form of somewhat flattened ovals. One of these beetles, however, is not at all flattened. It has the form of a short and very rounded oval, and its underside bulges so much that it looks like a little squat egg. The scientific name of the beetle is *hyphydrus ovatus*—it has no English name, but *ovatus* means *egg-like;* and it is bright rusty-brown in color. This little beetle can maneuver remarkably well, and it has the habit of swimming in rapid twists, circles, and figures of eight, just above the gravel of the aquarium, as if it were searching desperately for something it had dropped. The other water beetle is of normal shape and rather pretty, being yellow with black oblong spots.

The rest of the carnivorous water beetles that I find vary between an eighth to under a tenth of an inch in length. The larger ones are plain brown, but the smaller kinds are black with red, orange, or yellow markings, usually in the form of four squarish dots on their wing covers. These tiny beetles are

hyphydrus ovatus

extremely abundant and active. They feed on various water creatures of more or less microscopic size. Small as the beetles are, they do much to enliven the aquarium as they glide here and there with rapidly beating hind legs.

The larvae of all carnivorous water beetles are longish, pale-colored creatures, more or less like smaller, less fearsome specimens of the great diving beetle larva which I described in Chapter III. They breathe free air through two spiracles at the hind tip of their abdomens, and climb up water plants to obtain it. When ready to turn into pupae, they leave the water and burrow in the damp soil bordering their pond.

A curious thing about the larvae of all carnivorous water beetles that their mouths cannot be opened, for their lips are sealed. To compensate for this, each of their curved and needle-sharp jaws is hollow, and has a channel which runs from the mouth and opens at the tip. When the jaws of the water beetle larva have pierced its prey, a digestive juice is sent through the channels into the victim's body. The juice turns the victim's inside to liquid, which is then sucked in through the larva's jaws, leaving an empty skin when the meal is finished.

Closely related to the carnivorous water beetles are the haliplid beetles. These are all very small water beetles, about a tenth of an inch in length. Haliplid beetles are not so perfectly fitted for underwater life as the carnivorous water beetles. For instance, whereas the outline of a carnivorous water beetle makes a clean, unbroken curve from the front of its head to the hind end of its abdomen, the head of a haliplid beetle is quite distinct, and its edges are not flush with the edges of its thorax. Thus it is less streamlined and offers more resistance to the

haliplid beetle

water. Also, the hind legs of a haliplid beetle are not particularly oar-like, and look much like those of land beetles.

A carnivorous water beetle swims by kicking backward with the middle and hind legs of both sides of its body at the same time. A haliplid beetle, on the other hand, uses all its legs in swimming and moves them alternately. Although it can swim quite well, when doing so, the haliplid beetle appears to be running very fast through the water.

Haliplid beetles are mostly yellowish-brown in color, marked with faint lines or dots. Their bodies are rather broad just behind the thorax and taper sharply toward the hind end. These beetles are very abundant in weedy ponds. Despite their kinship with carnivorous water beetles they are not flesh-eaters, but feed on the rather simple kind of water plants that form green floating masses of fine, slimy threads, and are often known as pond scums. In my aquarium, the haliplid beetles perform a useful service by feeding on the microscopic green plants that smear the glass sides.

The water scavenger beetles belong to an entirely different family of beetles, all of which are rather poor swimmers. These beetles are generally oval in shape and very curved above but flat below. They carry their air supply on the underside of their bodies. The antennae of water scavenger beetles differ from those of carnivorous water beetles in being short and swollen at the tip, so that they look like little clubs. Their legs are not specially adapted in form for swimming, though in some kinds the middle and hind pairs have a slight fringe of hairs. The beetles swim with an ordinary walking or running motion. Adult water scavenger beetles feed chiefly on the decaying leaves of water plants and other debris, but their larvae, which have sharp, piercing jaws, are usually carnivorous.

Water scavenger beetles take in air from the surface by a special method: many of them use their antennae to obtain free air. When one of these beetles wishes to renew its supply, it climbs up a plant stem, or floats to the surface by letting go of whatever it is clinging to, and breaks the surface-film with its antennae. The antennae have microscopic unwettable hairs to trap a film of air, which connects with the bubble on the beetle's underside. Other water scavenger beetles simply push the front of their bodies above the water to take in air.

Hydrobius fuscipes, one of these water scavenger beetles (see Chapter III), is very common in ponds where there are plenty of water plants. In the aquarium it clambers among the water plants or

wanders around the sides just below the water surface, stopping to feed on any bits of floating plant refuse in its path. The air-bubble on its underside makes it appear silver as it crawls along the front glass. When moving across an open space between two groups of water plants, the beetle either crawls upside down on the surface-film or paddles along, back uppermost, just below the surface. It is unable to swim even an inch downward through the water, but

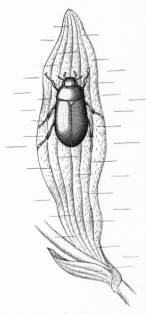

hydrobius fuscipes

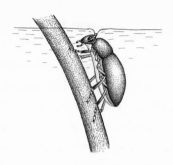

hydrobius fuscipes *renewing its air supply*

must descend the stems of water plants to get below.

Another water scavenger beetle that I often find crawling among tangled water plants near the edge of ponds is about the same length as *hydrobius,* but has a narrower, less oval body, and is yellowish-brown in color. This beetle has slender legs and never swims, but crawls upside down along the surface-film when crossing an open space of water. It flies readily on warm sunny days and I have frequently caught one in the air, sometimes a good distance from water.

Water scavenger beetles belong to a family of beetles that live, generally, in damp places. Some of them inhabit the wet vegetation surrounding ponds and streams. Others live in compost heaps and clumps of rotting plants, and I have found several kinds in lush meadows, crawling about on moist cow paths or burrowing within them.

It was probably in places like these many millions of years ago that beetles of this family developed a pelt of waterproof hairs on their undersides to keep them dry and prevent their spiracles from getting clogged. This would have made it a fairly easy matter for some of their kind to take a step further and actually enter the water of weedy ponds and take up life there.

11. The Crustaceans

Crustaceans form a large group of creatures with shell-like skins, nearly all members of which live in water. The woodlice of our gardens are among the very few exceptions. Most of the larger crustaceans, such as lobsters and crabs, live in the sea. However, there are many small freshwater kinds to be found in ponds and slow streams.

Unlike the insects, which always have one pair of antennae and six legs, crustaceans have two pairs of antennae and varying numbers of legs according to their kinds. Crabs and lobsters, for instance, have five pairs of legs, but woodlice have seven pairs. Crustaceans also differ from insects in that, apart from minute forms which can absorb dissolved oxygen through their skins, they all breathe through gills. Adult insects, and the great majority of their young, breathe free air through spiracles and air tubes in their bodies. Caddisfly larvae, and dragon-fly and mayfly nymphs are exceptional in being gill-breathers.

The largest pond crustaceans are the water lice. You are likely to find numbers of these crawling

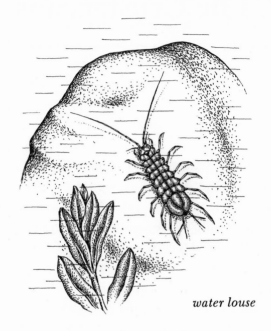

water louse

among the water plants that you pull up from your pond. If you run your net over the muddy bottom of the pond you will probably collect many more, for they are extremely common.

The males of water lice, when fully grown, are about three-fifths of an inch in length and the females somewhat smaller. Both sexes are darkish-gray above and grayish-white underneath, and they look like rather slender woodlice with long legs and antennae. Indeed, they are closely related to the woodlice.

If you put one of your water lice in a saucer of water when you get home, then examine it under a pocket lens, you will see that its body is made up of a number of segments. The front segment is the head, which has a pair of small black eyes and two pairs of antennae, the inner pair long and the outer pair short. The minute mouth parts are under the head and cannot be seen from above. The next seven segments make up the thorax and each segment bears a pair of legs. The last segment, which looks like a broad, flat disc, forms the upper surface of the abdomen. There are five thin plate-like gills attached to the underside of the abdomen. These, of course, cannot be seen from above, but you will notice a pair of leg-like tailpieces with forked tips protruding from the rear of the covering disc.

When you have dropped the water louse back into the aquarium, you will see it wave and lash its seven pairs of legs through the water. However, water lice are unable to swim and the action merely sends this one slightly forward as it sinks to the bottom. On touching bottom it will probably scuttle out of sight under the nearest stone.

The water lice in my aquarium spend most of the day resting in their dark retreats under the larger stones, but in the evening they come out to explore and feed. Then they walk over the gravel on tiptoe, with their bodies held high on their long legs. They also climb over the stones and up the stems of water plants.

When a water louse walks along the top of one

of the large stones, or rests there for a few minutes, I get a good side view of the creature. From this angle its body appears to be almost paper-thin, and I wonder how on earth the stomach, heart, and other organs can possibly fit inside it. I can now clearly see the five gill plates on the underside of its abdomen. These flicker rapidly to and fro with a constant motion to keep a current of fresh water flowing past them.

Water lice are scavengers and feed on any decaying plant and animal matter they find between the gravel stones. They nibble at the dead worms and pieces of potato peel that I put in the aquarium from time to time. They also browse on the green film that grows on the larger stones and the aquarium sides, and nibble the surfaces of water plant stems and leaves.

I quite often see a large male water louse make a sudden dart at another nearby and try to clutch it. If this also happens to be a male, it promptly scuttles out of the way, but a female sometimes lets itself be taken. The female water louse is then carried about under the thorax of her larger mate until she is ready to lay her eggs. The eggs, which have been fertilized by the male, are laid into a brood-pouch under the front part of her body. It is easy to see when a female water louse is carrying eggs because these show as a white swelling between her first four pairs of legs.

The young, on hatching, remain in the brood-pouch for a short time until they are developed enough to be set free. When first released from their mother's brood-pouch, these infant water lice are very difficult to see, for they are colorless and quite transparent.

Another crustacean you are likely to find is the freshwater shrimp, for it is common in ponds and particularly abundant in slow streams.

The freshwater shrimp is rather badly named, for it is not at all closely related to the true shrimps which live in the sea, nor does it look like them. It is, however, a near relation of the sand hoppers which burrow out of sight above high tide line, then suddenly appear and start hopping around when you disturb their homes by sitting or lying on the sand. The freshwater shrimp looks very like a sand hopper and is about the same size; but, while the sand hopper stands upright and moves by walking a few steps, then leaping forward, the freshwater shrimp both rests and moves on its side when it is not actually swimming.

freshwater shrimp

The freshwater shrimp is flattened from side to side, unlike the water louse, which is flattened from above and below. The shrimp is able to scuttle along on its side because the last three of the seven pairs of legs on its thorax are bent back and point the other way from the rest. These last three pairs of legs are fairly long and extend beyond the creature's back, so that it is supported and properly balanced by the opposite pointing legs of its down-facing side.

While at rest, or crawling over the gravel or stones in my aquarium, the freshwater shrimp holds itself in a very curved position. The thorax of seven close-fitting segments arches smoothly backward from its head, while the abdomen of six smaller segments curves abruptly down, then forward. The head itself bears a pair of small black eyes, the mouth parts, and two pairs of antennae—a long pair pointing forward, and just below this a thicker, down-curving pair.

The seven pairs of legs on the thorax of the water louse are all very much alike, but the thoracic legs of the freshwater shrimp differ according to their position. The first four pairs are fairly short and have gills attached to the inner side at their bases. Of these, the first two pairs are club-shaped with clasping claws that fold against their tips. These legs are used for handling morsels of food and lifting them to the mouth parts. The third and fourth pairs are of normal shape, and behind them are the longish uptilted legs.

Under the first three segments of the freshwater

freshwater shrimp swimming

shrimp's abdomen are three pairs of slender, branched legs known as swimmerets. The swimmerets beat rapidly backward in unison to propel the creature through the water as it swims. When the shrimp is resting or crawling about, however, they beat forward with a steady, flickering motion to drive water over the gills on its thoracic legs. The abdomen ends in a pair of flattened tailpieces, which together form a small tail-fin; and on the segments in front of this are two pairs of short stiff legs. These are used in a jumping takeoff that shoots the freshwater shrimp up from a stone or any surface to get it waterborne for swimming.

When they move in a hurry over the aquarium

floor, my freshwater shrimps swim on their sides, just skirting the gravel, and propel themselves along with backward flips of the abdomen and tail-fin. Sometimes they cruise through the water on their backs by kicking back and downward with their thoracic legs as the swimmerets drive them forward, aided by occasional back-flips of their tail-ends. However, when swimming fast and in earnest, the freshwater shrimps travel the right way up with a smooth and beautiful motion, using their fast-vibrating swimmerets alone, while their bodies are extended and almost straight.

Freshwater shrimps are lively creatures and interesting to watch, especially in the evening when most of them are active. They scuttle on their sides over the aquarium floor, stopping here and there to investigate and nibble at bits of debris among the gravel stones. Now and then one of them will leap up, straighten its body and swim in a neat curve through the water. As it descends and settles, perhaps at the other end of the aquarium, it immediately curls its body and sidles forward. Again it starts probing the debris with its little club-shaped front legs and poking inquisitive antennae down between the gravel stones.

Now it side-crawls up the largest stone, and disturbs a mayfly nymph, which leaps up and darts the length of the aquarium with lightning flips of its three-pronged tail. Equally startled, the fresh-

water shrimp slithers down the face of the stone,
then leaps up, swims to the side of the aquarium,
and lands on the shell of a large ramshorn snail.
The ramshorn continues crawling peacefully up
the glass until the freshwater shrimp pokes its
lower antennae under the shell's rim. As the snail
feels the touch of antennae on its sensitive skin it
slams its shell forward over its head firmly against
the glass, trapping one of the freshwater shrimp's
antennae. The freshwater shrimp struggles until
the ramshorn relaxes its grip on the glass, then it
darts down and scuttles under a stone. Four minutes
later, having forgotten its recent adventures, the
freshwater shrimp comes out of hiding, scuttles up
the side of the stone, waves its long upper antennae
to test the scents in the water, then swims to a branch
of Canadian pondweed and curls around the base of
a leaf.

Freshwater shrimps feed on any decaying plant
and animal debris, as well as living plants, young
tadpoles and other small, soft-bodied creatures.
They like dead worms, and sometimes succeed in
pulling one under a large stone, out of reach of some
other creatures that would share it with them. They
also like potato peel, and when biting into its large
surface they hold themselves upright instead of on
their sides. I have sometimes seen the piece of
potato peel that I dropped in the aquarium completely covered by two ranks of freshwater shrimps

standing shoulder to shoulder, with their heads down, as they nibble its white inner surface. They nibble the green film on the glass and stones in the aquarium, and bite into the stems and leaves of water plants.

My freshwater shrimps sometimes slightly annoy me, in fact, by biting through the stems of water plants that I have tied to a stone sinker, so that the plants come floating to the surface again. No doubt they sometimes annoy certain caddisfly larvae, too, by biting away some of the plant material of which their cases are built. I have seen a freshwater shrimp eat a young caddisfly larva, but I think it did so more or less by accident. The freshwater shrimp started by eating the case of slender plant stems, and did not stop when it came to the juicy larva inside.

When I was a boy I used to enjoy cleaning the watercress for salad meals. I eagerly unwrapped the bundles and separated the tangles of stems in the water, watching for the few freshwater shrimps that nearly always came catapulting out from the cress and went careering around the basin. These days, however, the neat bundles of watercress that I buy, firmly bound with elastic bands, conceal no freshwater shrimps among their leaves, and washing them is a dull, unexciting procedure. The growers of watercress beds have successfully made war on the little freshwater shrimps, which otherwise sometimes nibble and damage the young plants.

Male freshwater shrimps vary in color from light brown to gray and slate-blue, but the smaller females are usually reddish-brown. A fully grown male will clutch at any other freshwater shrimp that comes within range. If this is another male, it kicks and struggles and is then released; but a female, on feeling herself clutched, will usually curl her body tightly and remain still. She is then picked up and carried about by the male, who holds her securely between his first four pairs of legs.

The female freshwater shrimp, like the female water louse, lays her eggs into a brood-pouch under her thorax; and her young, on hatching, are kept within the pouch for the first few days.

All the other pond crustaceans are very small and can only be seen in detail with a pocket lens. After every pond-dipping expedition you are sure to see some of these small crustaceans swimming about in the pond water that you bring home. Others will swim out from the water plants that you place in the aquarium.

One of the commonest of the small crustaceans is the cyclops. This little creature is about a tenth of an inch long, and has a yellowish or greenish pear-shaped body. The broad end of its body is formed by the head and thorax, and the narrow end by the small abdomen which terminates in two short spines.

On the head of the cyclops is a single black or red eye which shows up very distinctly under a pocket lens. Behind the eye, and spreading outward, is a pair of long antennae, and behind this, a pair of very short ones. The cyclops swims quite fast in a series of short jerks by beating back the minute

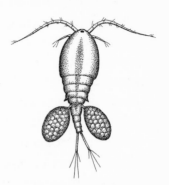

female cyclops with egg sacs

swimming legs beneath its thorax. It can also travel slowly by flicking its long antennae.

You will soon notice that some of the cyclops in your aquarium have a pair of oval objects sticking out backward from the sides of the abdomen. These cyclops are female, and the oval objects are their egg sacs. If you look through a pocket lens at a female cyclops resting against the aquarium glass, you may just manage to see the cluster of pinkish eggs tightly packed in her egg sacs. The eggs hatch into minute larvae that look quite different from the adult cyclops, but you would need a microscope to see them clearly.

Cyclops swim rapidly for short distances, then settle and jerk themselves slowly over the gravel or the surfaces of stones and water plants in a search for microscopic particles of food. There are other oval, brownish-yellow creatures in my aquarium, slightly larger than cyclops, which never seem to settle, but spend their time jerking up and down in mid-water. These are water fleas.

Water fleas are no relations of the true fleas that are found on dogs, cats, and sometimes, humans. True fleas are wingless insects, but water fleas, so called because they seem to jump up and down in the water, are crustaceans.

Water fleas do not swim about, but remain in a jerking cluster in one part of the aquarium. The whole cluster may change its position during the day, according to where the light is coming from. Water fleas like to be in a good light, but if the light gets too bright they all move to a new position where the amount is just right for them. They keep their position in mid-water by jerking themselves up with a downward beat of their branched antennae, then sinking back to where they were before and jerking themselves up again. The little creatures seem to be engaged in a life-long struggle to prevent themselves from sinking.

The head of the water flea bears the branched antennae used for swimming, a single, conspicuous black eye, and the mouth below. The rest of its body, including the legs, is enclosed in a shell or carapace which folds over the back and covers the sides. The two free edges of the carapace leave an open slit under the water flea's body.

As the water flea jerks up and down in mid-

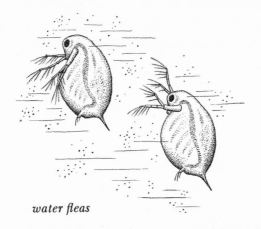

water fleas

water, its five pairs of tiny legs, which are fringed
with microscopic hairs, vibrate to and fro, causing a
current of water to pass through the carapace. This
current supplies the little creature with fresh water
for breathing and also brings in a supply of microscopic floating plants which are trapped by the hairs
fringing its legs and passed forward to its mouth.
The water flea filters its food from mid-water as it
swims and breathes, and it has to do all of these
things together.

12. Leeches and Flatworms

My mother was quietly writing a letter at her desk when there was a sudden *plop* in front of her. She looked up and saw a dark, wet object on her writing desk. The object was alive. It slowly uncurled itself, lifted its head end, then stretched forward toward her—becoming three, four, five inches long. As it extended it became thinner. It then fixed its head end to the desk just in front of her writing pad, shortened its wet body, pulled its rear end up, and fixed it down behind the head. It was now in the form of a plump, upward-bent loop. Again it lifted its head end from the desk, waved it in the air, then stretched forward and fixed it firmly to the blotter of my mother's writing pad.

What my mother did then I do not remember, for this happened a long time ago when I was a small boy. However, I am sure she took the incident calmly and in good spirit, for she was used to surprises of that kind. I am sure, too, that the leech, for such it was, was restored safely to the globe aquarium that stood on the shelf above my mother's writing desk. No doubt, as a precautionary measure, a cover of some sort was then found and placed over the aquarium.

The particular leech that climbed out of my aquarium and fell on my mother's writing desk was a horse leech—the largest of our common freshwater leeches. The horse leech is dark olive green above with two rows of black spots along its back, and paler brownish-green below. It looks like a dark-colored worm; and leeches are, in fact, worms of a special kind. They differ from earthworms in that their bodies are slightly flattened instead of being cylindrical, and quite smooth instead of having tiny bristles on the underside. The rings around the bodies of leeches are much closer together and less distinct than those around the bodies of earthworms; and leeches, unlike earthworms, have eyes on top of the head. The most noticeable way in which leeches differ from earthworms, however, is in having two disc-like suckers, one at each end, with which they cling firmly to any surface. The front sucker is small in most leeches. It is placed directly under the head and surrounds the mouth. The rear sucker is fairly large, wider than the hind tip of the leech's body, and visible from above.

A full-grown horse leech is a plump oval object, about an inch and a half long when contracted and resting, but can extend its body to a length of about five inches. When moving, the horse leech grips the surface it happens to be on with its hind sucker,

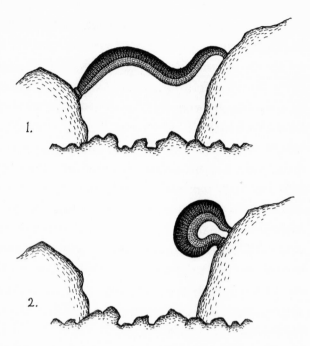

two stages in the looping movement of a horse leech

then extends its body and waves the front end about until its head sucker touches something solid. The leech then grips with its front sucker, releases its hind sucker, contracts and loops its body forward, and fixes the hind sucker just behind its front one. It then extends its body forward again and repeats the whole action. The horse leech is also able to swim. It does so by flattening its body further, and throwing it into a series of graceful up and down undulations which pass from the front end backward.

Many people think that the horse leech will suck their blood if it gets the chance, and are afraid to touch it. However, this leech is harmless and perfectly safe to handle, for its teeth are incapable of piercing human skin. It is not, in any case, a blood-sucker, but feeds on insect larvae, snails, worms and tadpoles, which it swallows whole. The only leech able to pierce the skin and suck human blood is the medicinal leech, which is now very rare in this country, and present only in a few districts. Medicinal leeches used to be quite common, however, and would fix themselves to the muzzles of horses and cattle that came to drink at farm ponds. As medicinal leeches and horse leeches are similar in size, the horse leech was wrongly blamed for this habit—hence its name.

Last year, when I was gazing into a pond, I saw what appeared to be a large, and very peculiar worm lying on the muddy bottom. The front part of the worm was of a very dark color and the rest of it the usual pinky brown. I bent down and pulled the worm out of the water. Then I discovered that the dark, front portion was really a horse leech, and that the forward end of the worm itself was already deep inside the leech's stomach. The rest of the worm protruded from the leech's mouth, and as this was as thick as the leech itself, the two creatures, one alive and the other dead, looked like one continuous form. So, having solved the mystery

horse leech eating a
drowned earthworm

of the strange worm, I placed it carefully back on the mud of the pond. Then I left the leech in peace, to digest its long way, slowly through its enormous meal.

Horse leeches are usually found on the mud at the bottom of ponds, but I have occasionally found them on land, resting under stones near the border of ponds. Fully grown horse leeches do, in fact, leave the water to lay their egg-capsules in damp soil. All leeches are both male and female in one; so, after mating, each is able to lay eggs. When the leech is ready to lay a few eggs, a broad ring of thin, horny substance is formed over a patch of skin near its front end. The leech then pushes the ring forward by muscular contractions of its body. On its way, the ring passes over the opening where the eggs are laid into it. It is then pushed off, over the leech's head. As this happens, the ends of the ring close up to form a capsule or cocoon containing the eggs.

Young horse leeches live very well in captivity,

and are interesting to watch as they loop along the bottom of the aquarium, or swim gracefully through the water. When they become full grown, however, they seem to find the aquarium too confining, and try to get out. The last full-grown horse leech that I kept spent nearly all its time half out of the water, sulking in a corner, up against the ledge that over-hangs the top of my aquarium. When in the water, it seemed restless and discontented, and refused to take any food. So I eventually took it in a jar and set it free in its home pond.

Common leeches, which are smaller and more slender creatures than horse leeches, are very plentiful in the ponds and slow streams near my home. I find them clinging to tangled masses of weed that I pull up from the water. They live very well in my aquarium and never attempt to climb out.

The common leech is reddish-brown, and about two and a half inches long when fully extended. Some specimens are faintly mottled with darker lines and spots along their backs. When I place a common leech in a saucer of water and look at its head end through a pocket lens, I am just able to see its eyes. I have to be very patient though, for the leech quickly realizes that it is trapped in a small volume of water, and pokes its head restlessly here and there as it searches for an underwater outlet. It makes no attempt to climb out of the saucer, however; it pokes its head up beyond the water rim only to withdraw it at once.

Eventually, by keeping my lens over the saucer, and taking advantage of every pause that the leech makes, I manage to get its head in focus for a few seconds at a time. I see its eyes as four tiny black dots arranged in a curve near the front rim of its head, with two on each side, behind the head.

Before the common leech becomes too distressed by its confinement and the strong light falling on the saucer, I return it to the aquarium. To do this I gently maneuver the leech onto my finger, where it clings very closely with its suckers. Then I take it across to the aquarium and dip my finger in the water. With my other hand I carefully release the leech's suckers from my finger, then watch it undulating through the water. It swims right around the aquarium, looping gracefully over and under the stems of water plants, then fixes itself on the front glass. Now I am able to see the small sucker under the leech's head as well as the larger rear one.

The leech crawls across the front glass, becoming long and thin, then short and thick, with each double sucker-step it takes. Every time it extends its body forward, the leech waves its front end first to one side then to the other. It is feeling for any nearby objects to which it can attach itself, before fixing its head sucker to the glass. Its eight minute eyes are of little use to it in this search, for they cannot see objects clearly, but perceive only differences of light and shade. At last the leech reaches a corner of the aquarium. It now crawls down to the bottom, loops its way over the gravel and disappears under a large stone.

The next day I see it again in my aquarium. Its hind end is fixed in the gravel under the edge of the stone. The front two-thirds of its body, now broad and flattened, is waving up and down with a steady rhythm. Loops of movement flow backward from its head, decrease in size, and disappear beneath the stone. The action is beautiful to watch. Its purpose is to keep a current of fresh water flowing over the leech's body. A leech breathes through its skin. When the water around it gets a little stale, it undulates its body. Gradually the leech absorbs a fresh supply of oxygen from the current of water

common leech undulating in its resting place

stirred up by its graceful motions. After an hour or two the movements of its body start to dwindle. Then, with its blood well charged with oxygen, the leech backs downs beneath the stone. It rocks its body gently for a while, and finally comes to rest.

One morning I noticed that a common leech on the glass of my aquarium was squeezed out of shape in two places near its front end. It looked as if two very tight elastic bands had been fixed around the leech's body, leaving a short gap between them. The leech was stuck to the glass by its hindsucker, and appeared to be in some discomfort. Its whole body kept revolving one way and then the other. Its head twisted about and tried to bend back to reach the pinched-in parts. I waited, almost expecting to see the leech break into three pieces. Then I noticed a kind of transparent skin covering the gap between the two constrictions. I realized that the leech was making its cocoon.

*common leech making
its egg-cocoon*

*common leech with newly
made egg-cocoon*

At that moment the kettle in the kitchen started boiling over, and the water sizzled on the stove. I hurried down to turn off the gas, and then filled the teapot. When I returned, the leech had cast its cocoon. The event I had hoped to watch took place during the few moments I spent in the kitchen. Now the leech looked quite normal, and fixed to the glass in front of its head was the newly made cocoon. It looked like a bluish, transparent balloon, and inside it were two white eggs.

The cocoon should have quickly shrunk in size, turned brown, and hardened to a horny covering for the eggs—but I realized that this would never happen. A young great pond snail was moving straight toward it. As the snail reached the cocoon, it opened its mouth and started eating. I could see the still soft cocoon-skin being drawn in, bit by bit, as the snail's mouth munched away. I watched the first egg drifting toward the steadily working mouth, and saw it disappear between the snail's jaws.

The leech tried hard to protect its egg-cocoon. It nudged and butted the snail with its head, and tried to push between the snail's mouth and the cocoon. But its efforts were useless. The solid and sturdy pond snail took no notice of the leech's prodding. It munched contentedly away until the cocoon was finished, then continued its journey across the glass. The leech remained, undulating its body over the place where its cocoon should have been. Ten minutes later it, too, moved away.

The common leech feeds on small water lice, young damselfly nymphs, little pond worms, and any dead creatures it can find. However, it has a small appetite, and abstains from eating for a week or two after each meal. It quickly scents the presence of a dead worm that I drop into the aquarium, and moves toward it. If the worm happens to be very small, the leech grabs it with its head sucker, drags it beneath a stone, then swallows it bit by bit. The minute jaws of the common leech cannot pierce the skin of a big, undamaged worm, however. It probes the surface of the worm with its head sucker, but has to wait until some water beetles have broken the worm's skin and made gaps in its body with their strong jaws, before it can take a meal. The leech then inserts its head beneath the worm's skin, tears out shreds of flesh, and swallows them.

The snail leeches are more difficult to find, for though quite common, they are inconspicuous and do not move when caught in the net. Sometimes I have not realized that I have collected one until I

snail leech eating a whirlpool ramshorn

see it on the glass of the aquarium, perhaps several days after my visit to the pond. It has come with a fresh supply of water plants that I brought home.

Snail leeches are broad, very flattened, and rather leaf-like creatures, from half an inch to about an inch in length. They are somewhat sluggish in habit and cannot swim, but loop their way slowly along when active. When disturbed they sometimes curl their bodies, release their suckers, and drop from their supports. They curl up when I hold them, and their bodies feel firm in my fingers, not soft and flexible like those of other leeches.

Snail leeches are almost transparent and of a pale greenish or pinky-yellow color. Some are marked with two lines of dots along the back. They feed chiefly on small water snails—hence their name. The head end of a snail leech, when extended, is very narrow, like the stalk of a leaf, and this is inserted into the opening of a snail's shell. The snail leech has no jaws or teeth, but it pushes a fine piercing tube from its mouth into the snail, and sucks its body juices. As the meal progresses the head of the snail leech goes gradually deeper into the snail's shell. When at last the snail leech withdraws its head the shell is empty of all but a fragile tissue of skin and solid parts. Now the snail leech retires to rest beneath a stone. It will not feed again for many days, perhaps for several weeks.

Flatworms belong to an entirely different group of creatures from earthworms and leeches. They are all fairly small, and look like flat, oval blobs of black, dark brown, or whitish jelly stuck to the undersides of the leaves of water plants that you pull up from the pond. You will also find them on the under surface of stones that you lift from the water. When extended and moving, they look like little flattened worms with rounded or triangular heads and bluntly pointed tails. Unlike true worms, however, their bodies are entirely smooth, and not ringed into segments.

Flatworms also differ from true worms in having only one opening to the food canal, and that is the mouth. This means that all undigestible remains of food must be excreted from the flatworm's body through the mouth. What is more extraordinary is that the mouth itself is not on the head of the flatworm. It is situated on the underside of its body, and about a third of the way up from the tail.

The flatworm is carnivorous, and when feeding on some creature, its mouth is pushed out at the end of a short tube. Solid particles of flesh are then torn out and sucked up the tube, together with the victim's body juices. The flatworm feeds on small, soft-bodied water creatures and any dead animal matter it can find. It covers a victim with its body, or twines around it and secretes slime over it to keep it still, then extends its mouth tube and starts sucking.

The flatworm finds its food by smell. The fleshy margins at each side of its head are sensitive to scents carried by the water. By turning its head from side to side as it moves along, the flatworm is able to track down its food. If the food is on the flatworm's right, for instance, the right margin of its head will smell the food more strongly than the left margin, and the flatworm will turn toward it. The eyes of the flatworm, which are on top of its head, can only distinguish light from dark, and do not help it in finding food.

When I drop a dead worm in the aquarium, my flatworms, which had been resting in various places, quickly wake up and start moving about. They wave their heads from side to side to test the direction from which the scent of the worm is coming, and finally discover its position. On reaching the worm they wrap their bodies around it, extend their mouth tubes into it, and remain still until they are fully gorged. When at last the flatworms move away to rest and digest their food—often on the sides of the aquarium—they look thoroughly bloated, and are twice as wide as they were before the meal.

However, flatworms are able to live a long time without food. Scientists have kept them starved, often for many months. During this time the flatworms remained active and healthy, but grew gradually smaller. They were able to continue living by feeding on the substance of their own bodies without distorting their proper shape in any way. After a long period of starvation the flatworms were quite tiny. To all intents and purposes they had simply become baby flatworms again, and when fed regularly they would grow up for a second time. I myself have not tried out this experiment, as I like to keep all my creatures well fed and contented as far as is possible. However, it is good to know that if my flatworms did run short of food they would not come to any immediate harm.

My flatworms spend most of the day resting under leaves, beneath stones, and in dark corners of the aquarium where the metal frame overhangs the glass. In the evening they wake up and go gliding smoothly over the gravel, up the stones, across the glass, and along the underside of the water-film. They glide about in a very mysterious fashion, without any visible means of moving. Even when I view an active flatworm under my pocket lens, I can see no muscular movements of its body. It simply glides forward, and perhaps bends its head gently to one side, then the other.

Actually, the flatworm's body is covered, particularly on the underside, with microscopic hairs. As these hairs beat backward with a continual flickering motion—only visible under a powerful microscope—they propel the flatworm forward. At the same time the flatworm secretes a path of slime over the surface on which it is moving. When a flatworm glides across the side of the aquarium it seems to be moving on the glass itself. Actually it is moving on the path of slime that it continually secretes, and its body does not touch the glass. This slime path cannot be seen on the glass, but when a flatworm glides along the top of a large stone I can just make out a very thin gap between the underside of the flatworm and the stone. The flatworm is moving just above the surface of the stone, on its slime path. The delicate, lashing hairs which propel the flatworm along would get rubbed off or damaged if they made contact with the rough surface of the stone.

A flatworm cannot swim, but like the bladder snail, it sometimes lets itself down through the water on a thread of slime, and occasionally turns before touching bottom and climbs back up the thread. One day I watched a flatworm in my aquarium let itself down a short distance, then climb up its slime-thread to the supporting leaf. A few minutes later the flatworm let itself down from the leaf again, then turned and started to climb back; but this time the thread broke and it fell gently to the bottom.

flatworm descending from a leaf on a thread of slime

Two kinds of flatworms are very common in the ponds near my home. One of these is a black, rather slender flatworm, about two-fifths of an inch long

*two common kinds of
flatworm in movement*

when fully grown. This flatworm has many minute eyes arranged around the rim of its head and continuing along the front margins of its body. The eyes, however, cannot be seen against the black of the creature's body, even with a pocket lens. The other common flatworm is dark grayish-brown and grows to about three-quarters of an inch long. This flatworm is fairly broad and has a bluntly triangular head with two eyes, set close together, on top of it. The eyes of this flatworm can be seen as two black specks, with the aid of a pocket lens. A patch of white skin surrounds the outer edge of each eye. The effect of this is to give the flatworm a peculiar, cross-eyed, and rather sad appearance.

There is a third kind of flatworm that I sometimes find, but which is not abundant like the other two kinds. This is the milk-white flatworm. It is milky white in color and grows to about an inch in length. There are two minute black eyes on top of its head, and its body is rather broad. The milk-white flatworm not only glides, but sometimes helps itself along by muscular contractions and slight

loopings of its body. It also undulates the margins
of its body in a rather pretty manner when it glides
along.

milk-white flatworm gliding along

13. Keeping It Going

I get endless enjoyment from watching the various creatures swimming, crawling, feeding, or simply resting in the aquarium-world that I have made for them. This small, watery world, charming and decorative in itself, is like the carefully chosen segment of a natural pond. The creatures moving freely within it are probably unaware of their confinement, and behave, no doubt, much as they would do in a state of nature. Their habits, their peculiarities, their changes in form during growth, the many ways in which they are so differently fitted to move and feed and cope with their surroundings—all these provide a challenge to anyone's powers of observation. They have made me realize how little I understand—how very much there is to learn.

I wonder to myself what living is like to a flatworm, with eyes that form no image of the objects around it, but only tell light from dark, and a body that glides along without legs, in a world where traces of scent in the water are of extreme importance. I wonder how it would feel to go buzzing, like a water beetle, through the air on a summer night, then dive toward the glittering surface of a pond, pierce it with my head, and go swimming in the dark world underneath. I try to imagine myself crouching as long and still as a dragonfly nymph, watching every movement around me, and waiting for my prey to come within striking range. I think of myself being as air-light and slim as a mayfly, and whirling upward then drifting down with outspread wings, among my fellows, in the glowing evening air. I enter the nearsighted world of a caddisfly larva, and imagine myself selecting objects, testing them for quality, then cutting them to lengths with my jaws, arranging them in a set pattern around my body, and fixing them together with a sticky substance from my mouth.

However, I cannot just sit back observing these fascinating creatures and imagining their lives. The life of the aquarium has to be maintained and kept in balance. Water plants get eaten away, and have to be replaced. At other times they grow too fast, and have to be thinned, cut back or taken out. The nymphs of mayflies, dragonflies and damselflies, and the larvae of caddisflies grow up and leave the water as winged adults. Then some new nymphs and larvae must be found to replace them. Water snails, flatworms and freshwater shrimps grow, breed, and increase in numbers. So some of these must be removed from time to time and then set free in some convenient pond. Other creatures get caught and eaten, or grow old and die, and new specimens must be found. So, each year I make new trips to the ponds and slow streams in the neighborhood, and I have the excitement of catching fresh supplies of creatures and releasing them into my aquarium.

From time to time a green film of microscopic plants threatens to cover the aquarium sides, despite the work of water snails and other creatures that feed on it. I have found that the best way of scraping this film off the glass is to use a single-edged razor blade. I keep a packet of blades for this purpose. I scrape the front glass of the aquarium so that I have a clear window to look through, but leave the green film to grow on the other three sides as an ever present source of food for the water snails, mayfly nymphs, and other creatures that require it.

The water itself starts to get misty with impurities and microscopic floating plants after a time, and has to be renewed. I use four feet of rubber tubing to siphon the water from the aquarium into a bucket placed below it. Before using the rubber tube I cut out a small circle from a sheet of wire gauze, bend it into the form of a bulb which is open at the top, fit this on the end of the tube, bind it to the tube with thin wire, and cover the joint and all but the base of the bulb with plasticine. This is to prevent water creatures getting sucked up the rubber tubing. Now I place the gauze-covered end of the tube in the aquarium, letting the rest of it hang down. Then, holding the free end of the tube over the bucket, I give it a quick suck to start the water flowing. I have a second bucket ready, and when the first one is filled I place my thumb over the end of the tube to stop the water flow, move the first bucket to the side, place the second one under the tube and release my thumb. Before the aquarium is emptied I pour a jugful of water over the gravel to set free the silt and fine debris from among its stones. This then gets sucked away before it settles again. It does not harm the water creatures to be stranded for a few minutes, but as soon as the aquarium is empty, I remove the tubing and start refilling it

base of rubber tube with wire gauze filter

from a jug. I pour the water slowly into a small tin or cup placed on the gravel floor. I have to make many journeys from the kitchen with the jug of water, but when at last the aquarium is filled and the tin removed, I can enjoy a beautifully clear view of my creatures in their setting of water plants and stones.

There are a number of creatures living in my aquarium, and many more in the ponds I visit, that I have not mentioned in this book. I have dealt with only some of the more conspicuous ones that you may find. I have not even tried to set forth a full life history of any of these creatures. Much more information about them can be found in other books. Instead, I have tried to show you how to start an aquarium, what plants and creatures to collect for it, and how to keep a varied company of these well balanced in numbers, so that all have a fair chance to survive. I have also tried to show you how enjoyable, and even exciting, the study of these creatures can be.

I now leave it to you to add your own observations to those in this book. I am sure you will enjoy making them, at the pond you visit as well as beside your aquarium. Above all, remember always to keep your aquarium looking as much like a piece of natural pond as possible, so that the creatures in it remain contented and feel at home. These creatures cannot tell you if the conditions are not right for them. They can only show you this by the way they behave, by their struggles to get out, or by dying. So study each kind very carefully, and try to discover, as far as possible, its particular needs. As you get to know the different kinds of water creatures, and learn something of their feeding habits, their movements, their likes and dislikes, you will become fascinated by them. You will go on making more and more observations, as I shall do, for the last word can never be said about anything so marvelous as a living creature.

Appendix

2. *An Expedition for Water Plants*

Page 23. Kingcup is a European Plant, but it has close relatives that occur in the United States, known as marsh-marigold or cowslip.

Wellington Boots are a type of British boot, excellent for shallow wading.

Page 24. All of the plants mentioned here have close relatives in the ponds and streams of the United States. Many kinds of water plants may be purchased at stores that sell aquarium supplies. They are called aquarium plants, or water plants, but the dealers do not usually know the different kinds.

Page 25. Brooklime is a common water plant. Its relatives occur around the world. In the United States it is called American brooklime.

Page 27. There are several species of duckweed to be found in the ponds and streams of the Western Hemisphere. They are all called duckweed. Only a botanical specialist can tell them apart.

Frogbit is the name of a British water plant. Similar species occur in the United States, and are called frog's bit.

Page 29.   Waterlily plants are large and not suitable for aquariums. They are grown throughout the world. The tropical species are much the larger.

Broad-leaved pondweed has its American relatives, floating pondweed.

Page 30.   Water crowfoot belongs to the buttercup family. A number of species of crowfoots are found in our ponds and streams.

Page 31.   Starwort and milfoil have related species around the world, and are called starwort and milfoil.

Page 33.   Canadian pondweed is widely distributed, and is known as Canadian pondweed wherever it occurs.

Moorhen is an English species of bird. The other birds have their American counterparts. They are grebes, herons, bitterns, plovers, snipes, and pond ducks.

Page 34.   Hornwort and curly pondweed, also called frog's lettuce, are English. There are close relatives in the United States, the American hornwort and curly-leaved pondweed.

3. *An Expedition for Water Creatures*

Page 39.   Pond skaters are also called water striders, or skippers, as well as other names. They belong to the family *gerridae*. The family *gerridae* is in the order *hemiptera*, or true bugs. It is a moderately large family of small- to medium-sized species with representatives throughout the world. Europe has over a dozen species, and there are about the same number in the United States. There is one genus, *halobates*, which is a true marine group of only a few species. They are much smaller than those in our ponds or streams, and are found in both the Pacific and Atlantic oceans, far from land. For this reason they are seldom seen.

I remember one occasion after a terrific storm on the Pacific. The next day dawned calm and quiet, but our expedition boat lay drifting. While repairs were made to the rudder, Dr. Englehart and I saw *halobates* species skating over the surface of the water around the boat. The captain very obligingly lowered a small boat, while we went around collecting specimens for a number of museums. These little creatures had withstood the violent waves of the previous day.

Page 40. Whirligig beetles are also called surface swimmers. Both names refer to their rapid gyrations on the surface of the water. The name of the family is *gyrinidae*. With over 400 known species in the family, representatives are found throughout the world.

Page 42. The backswimmer water boatman is not a true water boatman, which is another family. Most people prefer to call the backswimmer water boatmen simply backswimmers. They are the family *notonectidae,* which is in the order *hemiptera,* or true bugs. It is a fairly large family of about 200 species. It reaches its greatest development in tropical South America, but is well represented in the temperate areas of both continents.

Page 46. *Hydrobius fuscipes* is found on both sides of the Atlantic, being at home in Europe as well as in the United States.

Page 47. The three-spined sticklebacks, *gasterosteus aculeatus,* is found throughout the northern part of the Northern Hemisphere. In North America it occurs as far south as Virginia and California.

Page 49.   The great diving beetle belongs to the genus *dytiscus,* family *dytiscidae.* Species are widely distributed.

Page 51.   Caddisflies, freshwater shrimps, water lice, snails, leeches, mayflies, damselflies and dragonflies will be treated under their respective chapters.

4. *Tadpoles*

Page 56.   Tadpoles are the young of toads and frogs. They belong to the large group or class *amphibia,* order *salientia,* which means leaping animals. They are widely distributed around the world, many countries having their own particular species. A number of species are found in the United States. Frogs feel wet to the touch and belong to the genus *rana.* The toads belong to the genus *sapo.* Their original name, *bufo,* a more characteristic name, has been lost in the scientific shuffle of names.

Page 64.   Greenfly is a common name in Europe for aphids or plant lice. They belong to the order *hemiptera,* family *aphididae.*

Page 65.   Springtails are the order *collembola.* They, together with the order *thysanura,* silverfish, are among the more primitive insects, and are found in leaf mold or decaying vegetation.

5. *Water Snails*

Page 70.   Great pond snail. There are many species of freshwater snails which occur throughout the world. They all belong to the great phylum *mollusca.* A phylum is one of the main divisions of the animal kingdom.

6. *Caddisflies*

Page 85. Caddisflies are the order *trichoptera*. They also are known as cadices, caddiceflies, caseflies, and water moths. It is a large group of insects of over 3600 species, found throughout the world. Many species even occur in the colder regions and in high mountain ponds and streams.

7. *Dragonflies and Damselflies*

Page 98. Dragonflies and damselflies make up the order *odonata*. They have many common names, among which are ear sewers, devil's darning needles, horse doctors, and many others. It is a large order of over 4500 species. They are worldwide in distribution, the greatest number of species being in the tropics, with each country having its own group of species. They are very useful insects in both the nymphal and adult stages because they feed on mosquitoes.

8. *Mayflies*

Page 116. The order *ephemerida* has over 1200 described species, and there are probably many more to be described. They have many common names, such as dayflies and ephemerids, as well as local names like shad flies. In the Great Lakes area they are called Canadian Soldiers or Yankee Soldiers, according to where they seem to come from. If they drift south they are called Canadian Soldiers, and if they blow north they are called Yankee Soldiers.

9. *Water Bugs*

Page 129. Water bugs belong to the order *hemiptera,* meaning half-wing, because the base of the front pair of wings is hard and horny while the tip is membranous. Not all of the *hemiptera* are water bugs. The backswimmers belong to the family *notonectidae.* They are sometimes called boat flies because they look like boats and are able to fly. More than 200 species are known. They reach their greatest numbers in India and tropical South America. Europe and the United States each have their respective species.

Page 130. Water boatmen are the family *corixidae.* They are also sometimes called water crickets because they make a noise like a cricket. The family is small in species, but often numerous in individuals. Only about 300 species have been described. Water boatmen are distributed throughout the world.

Page 136. The water scorpions belong to the family *nepidae,* a small family of about 200 species distributed throughout the world. They are more plentiful in the tropics. Only 7 species are found in the United States.

10. *Water Beetles*

Page 144. Carnivorous water beetles belong to the family *dytiscidae.* It is a family of over 200 species found throughout the world, but chiefly in the north temperate zone. They have many common names, among which are dytiscids, water beetles, predacious diving beetles. The larva are called water tigers.

Page 150. The water beetles of the genus *hyphydrus* do not occur in the United States. There are over 50 species in this genus, and all are restricted to the Eastern Hemisphere. Closely related species of the genus *pachydrus* and *desmopachria* are found in the Western Hemisphere.

Page 152. The family *haliplidae* are known as the crawling water beetles because of their habit of crawling along the margins of the muddy banks of streams and ponds. There are only about 100 species in the family, with about 30 species found in the Western Hemisphere. They are delightful little creatures, less than a ¼ inch in length, and all look very similar until they are studied under a microscope. In the sunshine they gleam like little jewels. The pits on their wing covers are used as the basis of their classification.

Page 154. The water scavenger beetles are the family *hydrophilidae,* a large family of about 1700 species that are found throughout the world. They are more plentiful in the tropics, but are well represented in the temperate regions. Each area has its characteristic group of species.

11. *The Crustaceans*

Page 158. Most crustaceans live in the sea, but there are a few that live on the land and also some that live in fresh water. Species of water lice, freshwater shrimp, cyclops, and water fleas are widely distributed around the world, and any freshwater pond or swamp should contain specimens that are common to that area.

12. *Leeches and Flatworms*

Page 172.   There are two phyla of the animal kingdom represented here. The leeches belong to the phylum *annelida*. This phylum also includes the earthworms and other worm-like creatures. Leeches are not too common, but where they occur there will probably be more in the same pond.

Page 183.   Flatworms belong to the phylum *plathelminthes*. They are common in muddy pools or ponds, and are widely distributed throughout the world.

Index